# A MANUAL OF
# RED GROUSE AND
# MOORLAND
# MANAGEMENT

# A MANUAL OF RED GROUSE AND MOORLAND MANAGEMENT

by

Peter Hudson[1] & David Newborn

**The Game Conservancy Trust**
Fordingbridge
Hampshire, SP6 1EF
Telephone 01425 652381

[1] Dr. Peter Hudson is now at the University of Stirling

Hudson, P.J. and Newborn, D. (1995). A Manual of Red Grouse and Moorland Management.

© Game Conservancy Ltd 1995

ISBN 0 95001 130

Printed and bound in Great Britain by
BAS Printers Limited, Over Wallop, Hampshire

Published by
Game Conservancy Ltd
Fordingbridge, Hampshire SP6 1EF

# CONTENTS

**Chapter 4: Damage to Heather by Insect Pests and Frosting**

**Chapter 5: Bracken Control**

**Chapter 6: Grass Control**

## Acknowledgements

We would like to thank the following for discussions and helpful comments on the manuscript: Helen Armstrong, Flora Booth, Jim Briggs, Jamie Bruce, Brian Burrows, Len Campbell, Charles Connell, Richard Cooke, Nicola Crockford, Ken Dakers, Charlie Dent, Andy Dobson, John Drysdale, Graham Elliot, Sue Hartley, Graham Hirons, Angus MacDonald, Karen Laurenson, Ian McCall, Sandy Massen, Willie Peel, Dick Potts, Jonathan Reynolds, Pete Reynolds, Hugo Straker, Colin Stroyan, Mike Swan, Des Thompson, John Thornley, Phil Whitfield, Kenny Wilson and Michael Wood. Charles Nodder edited the text. The manuscript was prepared for printing by Judy Pittock, while James Long finalised the graphics. Our printers, BAS, were helpful throughout.

FOREWORD

# The Earl Peel
## Chairman of The Game Conservancy Trust


This book meets the urgent need for a clear, concise 'how to do it' text on red grouse and moorland management. Based on the diligent research of Dr Peter Hudson and the whole Upland Research team at The Game Conservancy Trust, it provides up to date, simple but scientifically-based guidance for anyone who needs it. I believe it will become the common denominator of grouse moor management and, in combination with the Advisory Service run by Game Conservancy Ltd, play a significant role in helping to ensure that our threatened upland habitats and species have a future.


In the decade since it began, the grouse research of The Game Conservancy Trust has achieved great things. It has confirmed many traditional management techniques as scientifically sound – and in so doing has provided a factual basis for their future defence. It has shown some management ideas to have been ill-founded and it has refined and improved others. Most importantly, perhaps, it has come up with efficient and effective new techniques for the management of grouse and of moorland. This book turns all that science into readable, practical guidance and I commend it to everyone involved in the conservation of the uplands of Britain.


Fordingbridge 1995

1

CHAPTER ONE

# An Introduction to Red Grouse and Moorland Management

## 1.1 About this book

This book is a manual – perhaps like a manual for your car or a recipe book. As a car manual is kept in your car and read in the garage or a recipe book kept in the kitchen and read while cooking, so this book should come to live in the pocket of your wax jacket or the glove compartment of your four wheel drive vehicle and be read on the hill.

You should look at this book when you are planning or worried about grouse management. If you are planning a day's heather burning then read Chapter 2. Check off what you need and what you should have ready for your first day. You may be worried about an overgrazed area of heather moorland. Is it really bad? What can be done? Read Chapter 3.

Each chapter is written in a series of sections:

**First:** Some background – what is the problem, when does it occur and what is known of its biology.

**Second:** Symptoms – how you can identify the problem and what characteristics to look for.

**Third:** Strategy of cure and prevention – the tactical approach, which techniques to use and when.

**Fourth:** Techniques – how to put techniques into operation.

Each section is written with bullet points – simply because a manual should not be a book of words but a book of action points. If you want to read a hearty essay on grouse and moorland management there are other books available.

Not all grouse populations suffer from the problems outlined in this manual but most will be affected by some of them; be they grouse in Yorkshire or Caithness. This book attempts to help you identify which problems are limiting your grouse population so you can do something about them. We have presented the practical outputs from the research efforts of The Game Conservancy Trust and others over the past 20 years. *Our* task is to identify the problems and develop the ways and means of solving them; the rest is up to you. Good luck! Remember that if you are in any doubt, Game Conservancy Ltd. has an Advisory Service on the ground that can provide practical advice whenever you need it.

## 1.2 Objectives of grouse management

- The objective of red grouse management is to provide a sustainable harvest of grouse from a specific area of heather moorland within a balanced package of multi-purpose land use.

- Multi-purpose land use involves the interests of shepherds, stalkers, and the general public who use the countryside as well as maintaining and enhancing the conservation interest.

- Most owners of grouse moors need to produce a reasonable bag of grouse, mostly from driven grouse shooting, although this may not be feasible in some parts of Britain given the constraints of the land and other management priorities.

- Multi-purpose land use is important for the uplands and there is no reason why good grouse management cannot run alongside other forms of land use including sheep farming, deer stalking, water catchment, and recreational activities, while maintaining the conservation interest. The only condition is that all parties fairly respect the requirements of other land users.

## 1.3 Priorities for the moorland owner, agent and factor

- The priority for the moor owner or manager is to provide a sustainable harvest of grouse within recognised budgetary constraints. The majority of grouse moorland is run at an apparent financial loss with some of the early shooting let and the owners taking their own shooting with friends at the end of the season.

- While the letting of the grouse shooting provides important income which helps to cover the keepers costs, many owners also encourage paying guests to stay in their houses and thus help cover the running costs. In poor years the problem is not just one of no income from grouse shooting but also one of no income from house lets.

- *Priority 1:* Given suitable habitat, the priority must be to employ a good and active keeper whose tasks are principally, if not solely, those of grouse production. Sufficient support must be provided for the keeper to undertake his tasks in an efficient and effective manner. If the habitat is not suitable, then *Priority 2* (below) becomes the first priority.

- Ideally one keeper should be employed to every 13 km$^2$ (3,500 acres) of heather moorland although this is often not economically viable in parts of Scotland. On isolated moors the keeper will have to cover a much larger area for predator control. Once the area of moorland exceeds 26 km$^2$ (7000 acres) then a second keeper should be employed if driven grouse shooting is the principal aim.

- Before going any further it is worth making the obvious very clear. When we refer to predator control we specifically refer to

5

the control of foxes, crows and other predators that can be legally controlled using legal techniques. We do not include protected species and we condemn the misuse of poisons.

- *Priority 2:* Ensure the extent of the heather moorland is not being reduced through over-grazing and poor burning practices. Negotiations with shepherds may be needed. Financial support for the control of bracken (Chapter 5), coarse grasses (Chapter 6) and for undertaking heather burning (Chapter 4) will be required.

- *Priority 3:* Financial support for the reduction of louping ill (Chapter 11). If this is a significant factor then this priority will rise to *Priority 2*.

- *Priority 4:* The grouse manager should ensure that detailed records are kept. These should include details not only of the numbers of grouse harvested but also numbers and whereabouts of predators killed and details of live grouse counts (Chapter 13).

## 1.4 Priorities for the keeper

- Given a suitable area of heather moorland, the task of the keeper is to produce a harvestable surplus of grouse by controlling the specific factors limiting the grouse population. Often the difficulty is to be able to identify which are the main factors that require action at any one time and of course to act before they become significant.

- *Priority 1:* Invariably this is the control of fox predation (Chapter 7) with action against crows during the spring (Chapter 8) and stoats (Chapter 9) during spring and summer. If the choice in spring is to go burning or catch a known fox, always go for the fox and leave the burning for another day.

- *Priority 2:* If louping ill is prevalent then actions against this disease should become the second priority. Specifically the control of mammalian hosts such as deer and hares, which sustain the tick population, together with vaccination and dipping of sheep (Chapter 11) .

- *Priority 3:* During the spring this will be heather burning but priorities vary according to the time of year (see Table 1.5).

- *Priority 4:* Long term maintenance of the habitat through bracken control and control of coarse grasses (Chapters 5 & 6).

- There are two main types of keepers who produce grouse. The first is a highly effective predator man who thinks and sees the ways of foxes and crows. Through his insight and respect for these predators he becomes highly efficient at predator control and produces a good harvest of grouse. The second type of keeper is rarer, he is a 'grouse keeper' who understands the ways of the grouse and the pressures upon the grouse population. He may well spend most of his efforts on predator control if he considers this to be the main pressure but he is thinking like a grouse and tackling the problems that arise for his grouse population. He knows and understands the behaviour or fires. These keepers are the great and exceptional grouse producers.

# Table 1.5: Priorities for the keeper during a year

■ High priority
▨ Low priority

| Activities | | Jan | Feb | Mar | Apr 1-15 | Apr 15-30 | May | Jun | Jul | Aug 1-12 | Aug 12-31 | Sep | Oct | Nov | Dec |
|---|---|---|---|---|---|---|---|---|---|---|---|---|---|---|---|
| **Heather burning** | **Chapter 2** | | | | | | | | | | | | | | |
| Preparation for burning | 2.6-2.9 | | ■ | ■ | | | | | | | | ▨ | | | |
| Heather burning | 2.10 | ▨ | ▨ | ■ | ■ | | | | | | | ■ | ■ | | |
| Cutting heather | 2.14 | | ■ | | | | | | | | | ■ | ■ | | |
| **Heather Grazing** | **Chapter 3** | | | | | | | | | | | | | | |
| Identifying overgrazing | 3.2 | | ■ | ■ | ▨ | | | | | | | ▨ | | | |
| Collecting heather seed | 3.10 | | | | | | ■ | ■ | | | | | | | |
| Growing heather plants | 3.7 | | | | | | | ▨ | ▨ | ▨ | ▨ | | | | |
| Planting seeds, seedlings | 3.11 | | | | | | | | | | ■ | ■ | | | |
| Sheep removal | 3.4 & 3.6 | ■ | ■ | ■ | ■ | ▨ | | | | | ■ | ■ | ■ | ■ | ■ |
| Hind cull | 3.6 | ■ | ■ | | | | | | | | | | | ■ | ■ |
| **Heather Pests** | **Chapter 4** | | | | | | | | | | | | | | |
| Heather Beetle: action | 4.4 | | | | | | | ■ | ■ | ■ | | | | | |
| **Bracken Control** | **Chapter 5** | | | | | | | | | | | | | | |
| Bracken spraying | 5.4 | | | | | | | | ■ | ▨ | | | | | |
| Bracken crushing | 5.6 | | | | | | | ▨ | ■ | ■ | | | | | |
| **Grass Control** | **Chapter 6** | | | | | | | | | | | | | | |
| Glyphosphate spraying | 6.6 | | | | | | | | ■ | | | | | | |
| Grazing of Purple Moor Grass | 6.6 | | | | | | | ▨ | ■ | ▨ | ▨ | ▨ | | | |
| **Fox Control** | **Chapter 7** | | | | | | | | | | | | | | |
| Snares & middens | 7.5 | ■ | ■ | ■ | ■ | ▨ | | | | | ▨ | ■ | ■ | ■ | ■ |
| Fox lamping | 7.6 | ■ | ■ | ■ | ■ | | ▨ | ▨ | ▨ | | ▨ | ■ | ■ | ■ | ■ |
| Hounds & driving | 7.7 | ■ | ■ | ■ | | | | | | | ▨ | ■ | ■ | ■ | ■ |
| Bolting foxes | 7.8 | | ▨ | ▨ | ▨ | ■ | ■ | ■ | | | | | | | |
| Tracing | 7.10 | ■ | ■ | ■ | ▨ | | | | | | | | | | ■ |

| | | | | |
|---|---|---|---|---|
| **Crow Control** | **Chapter 8** | | | |
| Making traps | 8.4 & 8.6 | | | |
| Larsens | 8.3 | | | |
| Cage traps | 8.5 | | | |
| **Stoats** | **Chapter 9** | | | |
| Tunnel traps | 9.7 | | | |
| Dogs & squeaking | 9.8 | | | |
| Mink traps | 9.9 | | | |
| Rabbit control | 9.10 | | | |
| **Strongyle Worm** | **Chapter 10** | | | |
| Worm damage | 10.2 | | | |
| Worm counts | 10.3 & 10.4 | | | |
| Direct dosing | 10.7 | | | |
| Ordinary grit | 10.9 | | | |
| Medicated grit | 10.9 | | | |
| **Control of ticks & LI** | **Chapter 11** | | | |
| Looking for ticks | 11.3 | | | |
| LI blood samples | 11.4 | | | |
| Sheep dipping | 11.6 | | | |
| Control of hosts | 11.7 | | | |
| **Insect Presence** | **Chapter 12** | | | |
| Checking for insects | 12.2 | | | |
| Artificial bog flushes | 12.4 | | | |
| **Counting grouse** | **Chapter 13** | | | |
| Counting grouse | 13.4 & 13.5 | | | |
| **Harvesting grouse** | **Chapter 14** | | | |
| Pointers & rough shooting | 14.2 & 14.3 | | | |
| Driven shooting | 14.4 | | | |

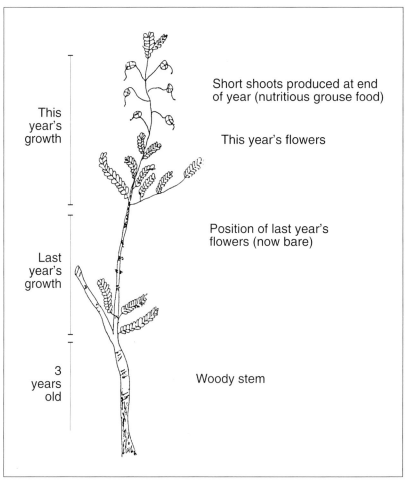

This
year's
growth

Short shoots produced at end
of year (nutritious grouse food)

This year's flowers

Position of last year's
flowers (now bare)

Last
year's
growth

3
years
old

Woody stem

*Ageing heather: a good understanding of heather growth is essential for assessing the impact of grazing.*
(After Mohamed and Gimingham 1970 (New Phytol.) with grateful thanks.)

CHAPTER TWO

# Heather Burning and Cutting

This chapter tells you why burning heather moorland is necessary (sections 2.2 and 2.3) and then provides you with the details of how to undertake burning (sections 2.7 to 2.13). It also advises when cutting heather may be an alternative (sections 2.14 and 2.15).

## 2.1 Heather growth

- Heather grows through four distinct age classes known as: *Pioneer, Building, Mature* and *Degenerate.*

- A balance of these age classes is achieved through careful patch burning and balanced grazing.

- Without fire, some seedlings will grow through the dying branches of degenerate heather but fire stimulates regeneration from roots and seed.

- Heather can be aged by counting the bare patches on the heather stalks where flowers have grown in previous years. This is best for heather less than 8 years of age; old heather can only be aged through counting the growth rings within the stems.

## 2.2 Why burn heather?

- Burning removes the accumulation of woody heather, dead shoots and litter; rejuvenates the heather stand and provides a structured habitat for grouse.

- Burning can sustain heather moorland and habitat for grouse by preventing the replacement of heather by other vegetation types.

- Burning provides edges, which are used as reference points by territorial cocks and are selected by hens for nesting.

- Young heather is nutritionally superior to old heather, having more nitrogen, phosphorous and potassium.

- Burning can provide fire breaks and reduce the risk of large scale fire.

- The production of patches of different aged heather attracts sheep away from the fringes of heather moorland where overgrazing can occur.

## 2.3 Burning and heather biology

- Burning stimulates seed germination and encourages shoot regeneration. After fire, regeneration from the root stock is the principal cause of heather re-growth from stands of young heather but seed germination is the principal cause from stands of old heather.

- In 12 year old heather, up to 58% of the stems will regenerate but in 25 year old heather only 10% will regenerate successfully, since plant stalks become lignified and thick. Furthermore, as the heather ages the ratio of wood to green material increases, making fire temperatures greater and causing increased damage to basal buds.

- In general, heather of age 6-10 years of age regenerates best from stalks.

- A successful fire removes vegetation above ground but leaves rootstock unharmed, usually protected by the litter layer.

- Seeds germinate after being exposed to a heat of 40-160°C (104-320°F) for less than 1 minute.

- As little as 30% of vegetation is burnt in a cool fire and as much as 90% in a hot fire.

## 2.4 Objects of burning

- To burn long narrow strips of mature heather on a rotation such that each patch is fired every 8 to 30 years depending on the build up of dead shoots and woody heather. Mature heather is that which grows to be half way up your wellington boot; if it has reached the top of your boot it should be burnt as a priority.

- To produce burnt strips ideally 20-30 metres wide and several hundred metres long.

- To burn the strips and produce a mosaic pattern of different aged heather stands within each grouse territory.

## 2.5 Dangers in burning heather

- Repeated burning depletes the moorland flora. Trees, shrubs and some herbaceous plants can be lost from the habitat.

- Fire resistant species such as purple moor-grass and bracken can be favoured and even dominate heather.

- When undertaken in conjunction with heavy grazing, burning may result in the replacement of heather with grasses.

- If the fire is too hot and the humus layer is lost nutrients can be lost from the moorland system.

- Frequently burnt peat can change its properties, become rubbery and reduce moisture penetration.

- Ignition of the peat can cause a serious fire hazard which is difficult to control and can result in serious erosion.

- Regular burning of steep slopes can lead to erosion.

- Encouragement of a pure heather stand can lead to soil acidification, leaching and thus soil degradation.

- Heather burning can be hazardous to people, stock, wildlife and the land.

## 2.6 Finance and burning

- Farmers may be able to claim grant aid for burning under the national Farm & Conservation Grant Scheme, issued through the Agriculture Departments (MAFF, SOAFD and WOAD). It should be emphasised that the grant system is always subject to change and this grant scheme is due for review in 1996.

- Farmers in some Environmentally Sensitive Areas may obtain grant aid for burning.

- Keepers will need to employ part time labour for burning.

## 2.7 Planning heather burning

- The Rule of Heather Burning: Select where to burn and what to burn. Never consider the hill as one large even heather stand. Be selective. If in doubt consult your Game Conservancy Ltd Advisor.

- As a priority select freely drained stands of heather on gentle slopes where the heather needs burning.

- Avoid areas with bracken. Do not burn into bracken stands particularly if they have a deep litter layer.

- Avoid steep and rocky ground where fires can lead to erosion.

- Avoid areas of wet blanket bog on deep peat.

- Avoid areas of conservation value especially where they include juniper. Take special heed if the area is part of an SSSI and examine the list of Potentially Damaging Operations.

- Avoid areas where heather is naturally short through wind exposure or wet.

- A steady annual burning rotation is optimal but this is not always possible. Always burn priority areas first.

- *Far better to burn too little and burn correctly than to ruin a hill through a careless fire.*


## 2.8 Fire beaters

- To control a fire it is essential for all workers to carry fire beaters. There are a wide range of fire beaters used and almost every estate appears to have their favourite.

- This section summarises the requirements and construction of five types of fire beaters, with notes on their advantages and disadvantages.

*Above left: Heather lighter suitable for starting fires.*
*Above right: Heather burning. Note the face mask, spark-proof overalls and bare hands to feel the heat of the fire.*

*Below: Well burnt heather moorland. Large stands of heather are broken up into a mosaic pattern.*

*Flexible steel fire beater*

- The head is made of flexible steel strips which allows it to put out fire on tussocks. It is made in Holland and can be bought direct from some agricultural agents.

- Advantages:
    Excellent for uneven and
        tussocky ground
    Light and easy to carry
    Robust and durable

- Disadvantages:
    Only a fire beater. Not good at snuffing fires
    Difficult to make – best to buy

*Birch broom*

- The old fashion forestry broom. Cheap to make and leave as a safety fire beater on the hill, particularly in areas where there is a fire risk from members of the public.

- Requirements:
    2m wooden shaft of 3cm in diameter
    Birch twigs 1m in length
    1.5mm steel wire

- Construction:
    Bind birch twigs to handle using wire to form a dense birch broom

- Advantages:
  Cheap and quick to make
  Raw materials easy to obtain

- Disadvantages:
  Birch twigs can catch light and burn during use
  Fire must be beaten; cannot scrub fire
  Rough on hands
  Not durable

*Flexible rubber fire beater*

- A cheap and easily constructed beater commonly used by keepers.

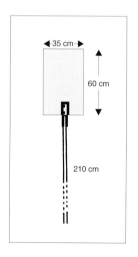

- Requirements:
  2-3m wooden shaft 3cm in diameter
  Conveyor belting 35cm x 60cm in size
  2 x 35mm bolts and nuts with large
      washers

- Construction:
  Drill 2 holes in shaft and conveyor
      belt
  Bolt belt securely to handle

- Advantages:
  Good on irregular ground
  Easy and cheap to make
  Light and easy to carry

- Disadvantages:
  Rubber beater will melt if too hot
  Cannot scrub out fires
  Beating fire can cause sparks and lead to fire jumping

*Steel pan fire scrubber*

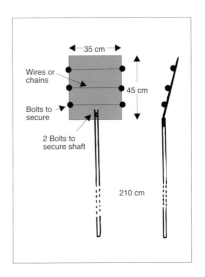

- Heavier than the usual fire beater but used to 'scrub' the fire out. Popular in Southern Scotland where the ground is not tussocky but dry heath. The construction notes tell you how to make one from scratch while a short cut is to buy an aluminium grain shovel, replace the handle with a long shaft and secure wires to base. More expensive but faster to make.

- Requirements:
    - 2-3m alloy shaft 3cm in diameter
    - 1mm thick metal plate 35cm x 45cm
    - 2 x 10cm steel tubing to take 3cm shaft
    - 3 wires or chains 40cm long
    - 2 x 35mm bolts, washers and nuts

- Construction:
    - Weld the 2 sections of steel tubing together at an angle of 30°
    - Weld one section of tubing to middle end of metal plate
    - Drill 2 holes in tubing, insert alloy handle and bolt in
    - Chains should be bolted to the plate
    - Wires may be looped through holes drilled in plate

- Advantages:
    - Good on short stands of pure heather
    - The wires scrub the fire out so there are few sparks
    - Safe and effective - robust construction

- Disadvantages:
  Heavy to carry and use
  Not effective on tussocky ground


## Weldmesh fire beaters

- A cheap and robust fire beater. Popular, and cheap enough to leave as a safety fire beater on the hill near areas of fire risk.

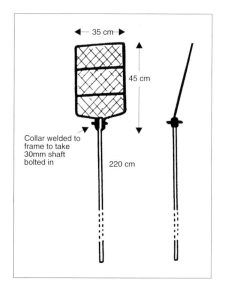

- Requirements:
  2-3m wooden shaft
    3cm in diameter
  10mm iron rod cut into
    3 x 35cm,
    2 x 45cm and
    2 x 20cm
  12mm weldmesh
    35 x 45cm
  10cm collar to take 3cm wooden shaft
  2 x 35mm bolts, nuts and washers


- Construction:
  Weld iron rod frame into shape of head
  Weld rods to collar
  Weld mesh to rod head
  Drill holes in collar and secure to shaft handle


- Advantages:
  Works well on pure heather stands and flat ground
  Best for snuffing fires rather than beating
  Cheap and robust

- Disadvantages:
    Weldmesh can result in sparks reigniting heather
    Of no use on tussocky ground

## 2.9 Before a day's burning

- Carefully monitor weather conditions in autumn and from January on, so you are prepared for a days heather burning if suitable conditions occur. Some of the best days are in late March but there are good burning days in February if you are ready.

- Take advantage of the increased evaporation rate from early March onwards; even a wet morning can be suitable for burning by the afternoon.

- Notify neighbours, hill shepherds and the fire brigade of your intention to burn. By law, neighbours should receive written notice 24 hours before burning. Confirmation by phone is often a good idea.

- Organise people into squads of three depending on burning conditions and their experience.

- Each squad leader should be told specifically which areas have been selected for burning and that they are responsible for lighting and tending their fires.

- Each squad leader should be fully briefed about fire breaks including lochs, roads, snow drifts, green runners, streams and man-made fire breaks. Man-made fire breaks can include areas previously burnt or swiped and free of trash and inflammable material. Ideally fire breaks should be 10 metres wide.

- If high pressure water pumps or foam are available ensure all equipment is serviced and working correctly.

- If heather swipes are to be used ensure all equipment is serviced and ready.

- Each squad should have one set of lighting equipment:
  matches
  heather lighter
  radio/walkie talkie/portable phone for safety
  spare fire beaters – preferably of two types

- Heather burner lamps are available from sporting shops in upland areas.

- Each person on the squad should have:
  a fire beater
  spark-proof overalls and face mask
  snack and bottle of drinking water

## 2.10  Lighting and controlling a fire

- Light the fire carefully, taking special heed of wind direction and fire breaks. The planned fire should be less than 30 metres wide. The length of the fire depends on the hill but is often more than 150 metres.

- Burn across slopes and downhill - fires tend to be drawn uphill and control can be lost.

- Ideally the wind should be steady but not too strong; the stronger the wind the shorter the burn.

- Light the fire across the wind in a strip about 15 metres in length to provide a face to the fire.

- If wind is light be careful, since the fire may generate its own draught and influence fire direction. Special care should be taken to ensure such fires do not become too wide.

- Once the fire is established, extinguish the windward side and let the fire progress with the wind.

- Members of the squad should then control the fire along the edges. Ignore the head of the fire but ensure the optimal width is maintained (less than 30 metres) and that the fire is guided towards the fire break. Controlling the edges is the key to fire control and producing a reasonable mosaic.

- The burning squad should keep pace with the front of the fire so the fire does not get out of control.

- Once the squad is watching one fire finishing, the squad leader can start the next fire but keep one squad member with the old fire to ensure the fire is really out.

- Do not have two fires close together – fire attracts fire and instead of two parallel fires the two come together and produces a pattern known as a 'pair of trousers'.

## 2.11  Dos and Don'ts of heather burning

- **Do** select areas of heather to burn

- **Do** notify neighbours and others of your intent to burn

- **Do** think 'fire breaks' – make new ones with back fires and know where fire breaks are

- **Do** ensure you have several squads of burners waiting for the correct conditions

- **Do** ensure all equipment is serviced and ready by early October and again by early March

- **Do** take note of conservation and archaeological areas

- **Do** return to fires to ensure they are out, sometimes the fire may get into the peat and reignite

- **Do** provide the burning team with spark-proof overalls. Ensure nobody is wearing flammable clothing

- **Do not** burn wet ground, screes or steep slopes

- **Do not** burn bracken, purple moor-grass or juniper

- **Do not** burn in strong winds

- **Do not** burn after sunset

- **Do not** leave a fire unattended

- **Do not** burn when peat is dry enough to light

- **Do not** leave this book too close to the fire!

## 2.12  Heather burning and the Law

- You can burn heather between 1 October and 15 April.

- You can burn between 1 October and 30 April on the authority of a proprietor or of the relevant Agriculture Department (SOAFD, MAFF, WOAD) above 1500 feet (450 metres), extensible with permission from the Agriculture Department to 15 May.

- Tenants must give landlords 28 days written notice of intention to burn.

- It is an offence not to notify neighbours with 24 hours written notice of the date, place and intended burning area.

- It is an offence to burn at night between 1 hour after sunset and 1 hour before sunrise.

- It is an offence to leave a fire unattended – you must ensure all fires are out.

- It is an offence to have a fire out of control or to be unable to satisfy authorities that all reasonable steps were taken for its proper control.

- It is an offence to damage woodland or neighbouring property with fire.

- It is an offence to damage ancient monuments through heather burning.

- It is an offence to break the stated prescriptions of heather burning on a Site of Special Scientific Interest. If in doubt check with your local officer of English Nature/Scottish Natural Heritage/Countryside Council for Wales.

- The Health and Safety Executive produce a guide for keepers and stalkers.

### 2.13 Fire control with high pressure hoses

- High pressure hoses with a water reservoir can be fitted on the back of all terrain vehicles such as Argocats, Land Rovers or Unimogs and provide a useful fire engine to control fires. Purpose adapted trailers can sometimes be used to transport the water reservoir.

- The great advantage of these fire engines is they provide a good safety back up, providing confidence for keepers to keep burning in dry conditions.

- The fire engines also provide an easy and fast way to get water to a fire out of control.

- Further information on this approach and the use of fire fogging systems can be obtained from: Scotkleen, Newmains, Strathclyde (01698 386555).

## 2.14  Cutting heather

- Cutting heather is not a good alternative to burning but in some situations (e.g. on areas adjacent to forestry) should be undertaken.

- Cutting heather can create fire breaks if all inflammable trash is removed.

- Cutting can stimulate regeneration of heather from shoots but cutting old heather may not stimulate suitable recovery from seeds.

- Cutting is relatively expensive compared to burning.

- Cutting tends to be more useful in the wetter western part of the country where the trash breaks down faster. It is particularly useful in areas where *Molinia* grass is mixed with the heather but has not formed tussocks.

## 2.15  Equipment for cutting heather

- Four-wheel drive tractors are usually necessary to pull cutting equipment on heather ground.

- Brush cutters or chain swipes are the cheapest but they do not remove the trash. A 65-horsepower four-wheel drive tractor should be able to cope with most conditions but a large swipe will need a more powerful tractor.

- Double chop forage harvesters will remove trash from the site but have the disadvantage of more limited access and will require an 80-horsepower-take-off from the four-wheel drive tractor.

## 2.16 Further reading

- Scottish Natural Heritage publish an excellent booklet on heather burning written by John Phillips and Adam Watson.

# CHAPTER THREE

# Overgrazing and the Regeneration of Heather Moorland

The aim of this chapter is to identify when overgrazing is a problem and then to present solutions depending on the type of habitat and the severity of the problem. A quick look at sections 3.1 and 3.2 will provide some background to the problem while section 3.3 guides you through a step by step action plan.

## 3.1 Overgrazing

- Heather is eaten by sheep, deer and other herbivores when their favoured grass species are either exhausted (August, September) or die back for the winter.

- Heather can be damaged through grazing and trampling. Both activities bruise and injure the plant so it loses water and must then use its reserves to mend itself.

- The greatest impact of grazing on the condition of the plant is usually in the autumn, often from late August through to October, although overgrazing can occur during winter and spring.

- The impact of grazing can be estimated by recording the amount of the current season's growth that has been removed from the heather plant.

- On average, removal of more than 50% of the shoots may result in the demise of the plant but this will vary from one area of moorland to the next.

- On dry heather moorland where growth is vigorous, the plant only starts to suffer when 40% or more of the current seasons growth is removed.

- On wet blanket bog the heather may not be able to sustain even a 20% removal of the current season's growth.

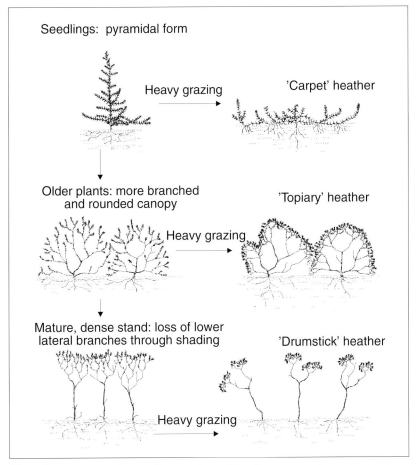

*The influence of grazing on the structure of heather stands: learn to recognise the various types and signs.*

(After Mohamed and Gimingham 1970 (New Phytol.) with grateful thanks.

29

## 3.2  Identifying overgrazing

- Winter grazing intensity is best measured in late winter before any growth of heather has started – early April is usually best.

- Identify vulnerable areas on the hill and estimate overgrazing within these. Vulnerable areas are:
    - (i)   stands of old heather near winter feeding areas
    - (:i)   stands of old heather mixed with grass or herb species
    - (iii)  young heather stands where there is a mix of heather and grass
    - (iv)  heather stands adjoining areas of palatable grasses

- The best method of assessing overgrazing problems is to be able to identify areas under risk and to watch and photograph them regularly.

- A more laborious but wider review can be undertaken. Walk a transect line through each vulnerable area and stop five times. Examine a one metre square of the ground and estimate the percentage of the long shoots of heather (previous season's growth) which have been removed (see page 10). Estimate an average figure for each vulnerable area and for the hill in general.

- If the area is on dry heather moorland and the percentage tip removal is in excess of 40% then this would indicate overgrazing while greater than 60% tip removal would indicate a heavy grazing pressure.

- On ground with a thick peat covering, a tip removal of more than 25% would indicate overgrazing, and more than 40% a heavy grazing pressure. Such estimates are coarse and would depend on the annual growth of heather.

- The period of overgrazing can be determined by describing the condition of the heather. Heather plants become distorted after years of heavy grazing pressure, since grazing animals remove growing tips, thus stimulating the growth of side shoots and produces a gnarled look to the heather. Heavily grazed heather is sometimes referred to as 'bottle brush' or 'drumstick' heather. Such areas should be classified as chronically overgrazed.

- The shape and structure of the heather changes depending on the time when the plant suffers from grazing (see page 29).

- Each area of vulnerable heather can then be classified as:
    (i)    Currently overgrazed
    (ii)   Chronically overgrazed
    (iii)  Previously overgrazed

A number of other signs also indicate overgrazing:

- In areas of heavy grazing, sheep will pull-up and then leave small heather plants, particularly in areas of heather burnt 2 to 5 years previously.

- When heather is being grazed heavily, the herbivores may be forced to take other species, even when their relative quality is worse than heather. For example *Nardus* grasses may be taken during late summer and winter.

- Bilberry (same as blaeberry) may be heavily grazed leaving it with few leaves.

- Grazing of heather has started by early August.

- Areas of grass are tightly grazed by August, often with abundant mosses and areas of bare ground.

- Heavily grazed areas may show a change in vegetation structure depending on habitat type. An increase in bracken, bilberry, cowberry, crowberry, cotton grass, purple moor-grass, *Juncus squarrosus* or *Nardus* are all signs of heavy grazing.

- Cotton grass can be particularly useful. An abundance of flowering heads or even seed heads (see Chapter 6) indicates low current grazing pressure, while few flower or seed heads implies continued heavy grazing.

### 3.3 Action plan for overgrazed heather

- First, examine the area and determine that overgrazing is the problem (3.2).

- Who are the culprits – sheep, cows, deer, rabbits, hares or is it a combination of species?

- Be careful since the removal of one species may result in increased grazing by another species (e.g. removal of sheep can result in increased deer grazing).

- Does the area have live heather plants present? This is best seen in August when the few plants may produce flower. If so, then the problem could be stock control (3.4, 3.5 and 3.6). If not, then the ground may no longer be suitable for heather.

- To determine if the ground is suitable:

(i) Cut 3 shallow trenches and determine if heather root stock is present, indicating the past presence of heather. If heather roots are still present then look more carefully for active heather plants. The better drained, steeper areas may still carry suitable quantities of heather and stock control may be the answer (3.4, 3.5, 3.6).

(ii) Has the ground been improved agriculturally through lime and slag? If so, is the pH acceptable for heather growth, or has there has been a long history of grazing?

- To test soil pH, send soil samples to a local agricultural laboratory or ask your Game Conservancy Ltd Advisor. A pH between 2 and 6.5 is suitable for heather, greater than 7 would indicate the soil was too alkaline.

- One quick and simple method to determine if the ground is suitable for regeneration is to fence a small area with a length of rabbit fencing and check for heather growth 6 to 12 months later.

- If the ground is suitable but no active plants are present the next step is to determine if an active heather seed bank is present (see 3.7).

- If a heather seed bank is present then this can be stimulated through the techniques presented in section 3.8, although some areas may need stabilising (3.12), and while more expensive, there is always the possibility of turfing small areas (3.9) or introducing seedlings (3.10).

- If no heather seed bank is available but the ground is suitable then seed (3.10 and 3.11), seedlings (3.10) or turves (3.9) can be introduced.

- Care should always be taken to avoid erosion problems, although small eroded areas can be returned to heather (3.12).

- Grant aid may be available for heather restoration depending on your circumstances. This may cover simply costs of fencing, or provide further incentives. The Farm and Conservation Grant Scheme, Moorland Scheme and special funding if you are in an Environmentally Sensitive Area may be available. Contact your local MAFF, SOAFD or WOAD officer for details.

## 3.4 Sheep stocking

- Sheep grazing intensity is a product of numbers, distribution and period of grazing.

- Higher sheep numbers can be sustained during summer than winter particularly if the hill carries a good mixture of grass and heather.

- Optimal sheep density, assuming an even spread of sheep varies according to habitat from 0.2 ewes per hectare to 1.5 ewes per hectare (0.08 to 0.6 ewes per acre) during the winter months. On average, heather moorland maximum stocking rates are usually taken as 1.0 to 1.5 ewes per hectare (0.4 to 0.6 ewes per acre) during winter.

- Optimal stocking density should be lower when:
    - (i)    The ground is wet with a thick peat layer
    - (ii)   There is not a good age structure to the heather stand (A good age structure has 20% or more of short, young heather)
    - (iii)  There are few quality grasses, particularly the fescues and the bents
    - (iv)   There is winter feeding of sheep
    - (v)    Sheep are not shepherded during winter

- Even with a low density of sheep, localised overgrazing will still exist when there is winter feeding which concentrates the sheep on areas of heather, particularly if sheep are not shepherded after feeding.

- It is always worth examining the tenancy agreements and rules of the Commons Committees (in England) to check on numbers allowed and shepherding rules.

*Above: Correct management of the appropriate number of sheep is vital. Hay should be placed in proper racks, and located away from heather ground.*

*Below: When a seed bank is absent it may be worthwhile drilling heather seed into white ground.*

- Most overgrazing on grouse moors exists as a consequence of winter feeding rather than high stocking levels.

## 3.5 Winter feeding of sheep

- Winter fothering concentrates sheep on certain areas of heather. Urea based feed blocks, can stimulate the sheep to eat more roughage, usually taken as heather.

- Winter fothering sites must not be placed on or close to old heather where trampling and grazing will kill the heather stand.

- Winter fothering sites should ideally be placed 250m from the heather edge on stands of coarse grass or areas of dead bracken.

- If feeding sites are on heather they should be kept on areas of young heather, and moved more than 250m each week.

- Replacement supplement blocks should be at least 250m from points used previously that winter.

- Farmers often place hay on old heather to prevent it from blowing away. The solution is to move the feeding sites and hold the hay in hay racks.

## 3.6 Heather regeneration through stock control

- Ideally, heather regeneration should aim to restore heather to a level where grouse and sheep can both be sustained.

- Grazing intensity should be reduced by decreasing sheep numbers during autumn and winter. Ideally this should be from 12 August to 1 May but at least from 1 September to when the temperatures rise above 6°C and grass species become available for sheep to feed on.

- Optimal stocking densities during the winter must be lower when damage to heather is severe, when there is little alternative food during autumn or spring and on wet acid moorland.

- Ideally, heavily grazed heather should be rested during the winter months for 2-5 years depending on conditions but such a system is not always practical.

- On areas severely grazed and on wet acid moorland, sheep should be removed totally in the winter but with a summer sheep density of 1 ewe per 1-2ha (1 to 2.5-5 acres) depending on the availability of suitable grass species for sheep to feed on.

- On areas of wet acid moorland with moderate grazing damage, a winter density of 1 ewe to every 2-4ha (1 to 5-10 acres) is suitable but no winter feeding should take place within 500m of the heather and sheep should ideally be shepherded.

- On areas of dry heather moorland with severe grazing, a summer stocking density of 2 ewes per ha (1 ewe to 1.25 acres) may be required to graze the grasses, with a winter stocking density of 0.5 ewes per ha (1 ewe to 5 acres).

- Areas with reduced grazing pressure may need to be fenced to prevent sheep from neighbouring areas moving in.

- Areas should be carefully monitored using fixed point photography (e.g. camera on top of same fence post) each March, and by careful examination of the grazing pressure on the recovering heather. Game Conservancy Ltd's Advisory Service can provide assistance with this task.

- A major problem in heather regeneration programmes is often where to move sheep during winter months. Possibilities include:

(i)   Away-wintering sheep to lowland farms

(ii)  Moving sheep onto low ground set-aside between 1 September and 15 January but farmers must use their own stock on their own set-aside

(iii) In-wintering sheep in large sheds

(iv)  Moving sheep to in-bye pastures

(iv)  Increasing grazing levels on other areas of moorland, although increased grazing numbers will require good shepherding.

(v)   Moving sheep to areas of hill ground where the heather has been lost or sacrificed to grazing animals.

## 3.7 Identifying a seed bank

• As a general rule, any area which was previously heather or down wind of a heather stand hould have a potentially active heather seed bank. Removal of existing vegetation can result in the regeneration of heather moorland from seed.

• To identify a seed bank take soil samples from various areas where heather regeneration is required. Samples should be taken from the top 5cm of soil and stones, debris and dead plant material removed.

• Mix soil material with John Innes No.1 potting compost (without lime) and spread on a compost mixture of John Innes No. 1 and 25% coarse sand.

• Ideally keep in a glasshouse with a mist sprayer which keeps the samples continually moist, but a light warm shed or even poly-tubes with regular spraying will suffice. Care should be taken not to waterlog the soil.

• Glasshouses should be kept at 18-25°C. Seedlings will appear after 6 weeks, 90% will have germinated by 12 weeks and seedlings will be ready for planting, if required, at 24 weeks of age after 2 weeks hardening. Fluctuation in temperatures between 18 and 25°C can aid germination.

- If no seeds are present after 12 weeks, mix the sample and start again, after this if there are no heather seedlings present then the seed bank sampled is exhausted.

- With more than 300 seedlings per square metre a suitable heather seed bank exists.

- With less than 100 seedlings per square metre the seed bank is insufficient to regenerate.

- If seedlings are subsequently required for planting then spread evenly in fibre pots or paper tubes, otherwise plastic seed trays can be used.


## 3.8 Stimulating seedling growth

- If a seed bank is present, germination can be stimulated by exposing seeds to light.

- The area to be regenerated should be stripped of vegetation to expose the seed but such action can lead to serious erosion problems. In these situations it may be necessary to use companion grasses to stabilise peat and obtain heather growth through the grasses (see 3.12). Alternatives are to scuff up sods with a heavy disc harrow or to cut narrow trenches in which to stimulate growth. Such areas should not suffer badly from erosion and the resulting strips of heather will establish heather dominance. Strips should run across the slope.

- Removing vegetation with herbicides is not successful in the long term since grasses can recover and swamp heather seedlings.

- Cut trenches 25cm across and not more than 4cm in depth using an adapted rotavator – a special rotavator machine for this task is available through Game Conservancy Ltd. Trenches should be carefully sited to avoid waterlogging or erosion. Larger areas may be trenched, depending on the rainfall and slope.

- Trenches must be exposed to light but not dry out, as germination occurs during wet and warm periods, principally in autumn and spring.

- At high altitudes, above 550m (1800ft), late spring and summer is better than autumn.

- Areas of heather re-establishment must be kept clear of all mammalian herbivores including sheep, deer, hares and rabbits, so fencing is probably essential.

- Care should be taken about the siting of fences since grouse and other birds can fly into recently erected fences, particularly young birds dispersing during the winter and when fences are hidden from the birds view. Corks, plates or luminous tape tied to the fence may reduce accidents.

### 3.9  Turfing areas of moorland

- Turfing areas of moorland is possible. Restoring heather areas after pipeline, quarrying or road construction needs special attention and the expertise developed by The Environmental Advisory Unit, University of Liverpool should be sought.

- Removal of turves can damage that area of moorland. Unless the area was to be destroyed for other reasons careful thought should be given to the consequences of turfing.

- Any turfing programme should be conducted in early spring or autumn.

- Turves should be of young heather 4-20 years in age. Older heather may be used with some success but will benefit from spraying with a transpiration inhibitor; ask your local garden centre.

- The turves should be cut to a depth of more than 30cm, the deeper the better to avoid damage to roots.

- Turves should be cut using a crawler mounted bucket with a smooth cutting edge.

- Turves should be carefully transferred between sites in a trailer and stored for the minimum time possible and not more than 3 days.

- Turves must be sited and placed in a manner which will avoid erosion and wind exposure. Turfing steep slopes is not feasible.

- Turves should be carefully positioned and can be interspersed with a background mixture of companion grasses, these will stabilise the peat and allow the site to blend well.

- Grazing animals should be excluded from turfed areas for a minimum of 2 years although if fencing can be avoided costs will be greatly reduced.

## 3.10  Collecting seed for sowing

- Heather seed can be collected either for growing young heather plants in glasshouses (see 3.7) or for spreading on prepared ground for heather regeneration.

- The most effective technique for gathering seed is to use an industrial vacuum cleaner or a cheap, hand held garden vacuum or leaf gathering machine. Some areas may require raking before collection to loosen the surface material and this can be undertaken using a 4WD bike with a harrow.

- Collect seed from recently burnt areas of heather where there is still a litter layer and the seed has been vernalised by the fire. Heather stands should not have been too old before being burnt, ideally 10-15 years of age.

- Within one day, one person should be able to collect 250kg of material – sufficient seed to cover 800 square metres.

- Litter layer should be collected when dry and vegetation fragments and dead material removed. Passing the material through a seed dresser will provide a clean sample.

- Seed should be stored in paper sacks in dry, dark conditions kept at an even cool temperature. Seed should remain viable for several years.

- If time allows, check the germinable seed content using the techniques described in section 3.7.

## 3.11 Establishing a new seed bank

- Establishing a seed bank is time consuming and only necessary when there is neither heather plant nor seed bank present. Seedlings can be introduced into areas with a seed bank for faster and more effective regeneration.

- Acid grasses should be removed from the area through scraping and the peat exposed to a depth of 5cm in depth.

- Erosion problems can occur, so is usually best to cut narrow strips about 25cm across into which the seed mixture will be introduced. Care should be taken not to cut these downhill or in areas where erosion or waterlogging will occur.

- A heather seeding machine is available, which will prepare the ground and introduce seed. For further details of hire, contact Game Conservancy Ltd's Advisors.

- If the area is not liable to erosion, then areas of about 50 $m^2$ can be scraped and treated in a mosaic across the hill.

- Litter should be applied in the channels at 1.0-1.5kg per square metre or at a level which would give 500 seeds per square metre.

- Seedlings can be grown in glasshouses (3.7) and introduced onto the scraped area where they can establish heather cover and a seed bed. This can be time consuming.

- Before planting, seedlings should be thoroughly soaked and care taken not to damage roots. Ideal density is 15 seedlings/$m^2$. Seedlings grown in glasshouses in biodegradable paper tubes and then hardened for two weeks and transplanted in spring can have a high survival rate. Once again, seedlings must neither dry out not sit in waterlogged soil.

## 3.12 Reinstating heather on eroded areas

- Exposed areas of peat can occur as a result of bracken removal, severe fire, pollution and trampling damage by humans, stock or machinery.

- Severe fires can result in the loss of the heather root stock and seed bed, and may de-stabilise peat leading to erosion and the exposure of underlying mineral soil.

43

- Before heather can be re-established on an eroded area, the peat must be stabilised.

- Areas to be treated will need fencing to exclude grazing animals for a minimum of 5 years or until heather is reinstated.

- On areas which have been severely burnt it may be necessary to break up the carbonised peat by shallow rotivation, tined cultivator or disc harrow. Great care should be taken to ensure this is not done too deeply leading to further erosion.

- At low altitudes, in sheltered areas peat can be stabilised by laying forestry brashings on the peat and then adding the seed mixture (collected as in 3.10) or topsoil.

- In more exposed areas companion grasses should be sown to stabilise the peat.

- Areas to be treated with companion grasses may  benefit from a more alkaline pH and should be treated with crushed limestone (2500kg per ha) and a compound fertiliser like ICI fertiliser No 5 (200kg per ha) just prior to establishment.

- Companion grass mix should include species which will stabilise the peat and help to keep undesirable grasses from invading but not out-compete the young heather plants. Suitable grass species include a mixture of  about 40% *Agrostis castellana* and 60% *Agrostis vinealis* sown at 15kg per ha. These seeds are available through commercial seed merchants.

- The area should be rolled so the peat is  moderately compacted. No great weight is needed and careful shuffling steps or driving a 4WD bike across the area should be adequate. A light roller could be used for larger areas.

- Peaty topsoil can be collected from adjacent areas after heather has been removed by flail mowing and then rotavated to a depth of 5cm. This topsoil can be spread on the area instead of heather seeds and will provide a good recovery, but may destroy the areas of moorland from which it is removed.

- Cut shoots of heather can be heeled in to the ground and will take under favourable conditions.

- In areas which have been bracken beds, any loose bracken litter should be removed together with any obvious roots or shoots before re-establishment.

## 3.13 Drainage

- Heather favours freely drained ground. Several estates have attempted to improve heather growth through drainage.

- Essentially drainage is not successful on wet blanket peat since the peat holds the water and the water table is only reduced close to the drain.

- In some areas, particularly at the interface of blanket peat and freely drained heather moorland, it may be possible to convert blanket bog to freely drained heather moorland but this is not recommended.

- Great care should be taken in introducing drains to avoid erosion. In particular, herring-bone systems should be used which follow the hill contours.

- Drainage may reduce bog flushes and other areas used by grouse chicks, see Chapter 12.

## 3.14 Grazing equivalents

The following coarse estimates of grazing equivalents on heather may be useful but are the subject of ongoing research.

1 cow = 12 ewes in terms of heather damage

1 horse = 10 ewes

1 deer hind = 2 ewes

5 hares = 1 ewe

8 rabbits = 1 ewe

# CHAPTER FOUR

# Damage to Heather by Insect Pests and Frosting

The damage of heather by weather or pests can seriously reduce the extent of valuable food for grouse and sheep during the winter. Action needed is first to identify the culprit and second to examine the possible ways of reducing the spread and curing the problem.

## 4.1 Heather damage – the first look

*   Heather damage is usually first noticed as areas of apparently dead or dying heather, often turning a ginger colour. In most situations the heather has died as a consequence of water imbalance initiated either by pests or weather.

*   Damage may act either on the roots or the green and woody vegetation above ground. When inspecting a damaged plant, remove it carefully from the soil and inspect all parts. In many cases the damage is only noted after the causative agent has departed, so look for both the damage and the possible culprit.

*   Damage is often worst in old heather where there is a high proportion of woody material compared with the productive green tissue. Recovery after an attack is more difficult for an old plant since regeneration from side shoots and roots is limited by the thickness of woody material.

*   The main agents that cause damage are:
    (i)     Fire – see Chapter 2
    (ii)    Grazing – see Chapter 3
    (iv)    Insect species – this Chapter
    (v)     Fungal attack – this Chapter

(vi)   Weather – this Chapter
(vii) Crushing and trampling by vehicles, animals or
people – Chapter 3


## 4.2  Key to heather damage

Identifying the causative agent will help greatly in solving the problem, if at all possible. Remove the damaged plant and then sit down
and carefully follow the instructions in this key. Note this key does
not include damage caused through accidental fire but is specifically
aimed at identifying insect and fungal attack. Start with question 1
and then follow the instructions, if you don't get a clear answer first
time through, try again or ask someone else to have a go.

*1.   Has part of the plant been eaten?*
No  = Go to 10
Yes = Go to 2


*2.   Has the bark been shaved from fine branches revealing white
wood?*
No  = Go to 3 but first look for other signs of heather beetle (see
below). You really need to convince yourself it is not heather
beetle before going any further.
Yes = This would indicate an attack by heather beetle. There may
also be some resprouting from stem bases. This will tend to
occur on heather in flat damp areas and usually at an altitude
of less than 300m (1000ft). The vegetation may also be turning a reddish brown. (For actions see 4.4).


*3.   If there is no bark shaved then could be winter browning:*
If not winter browning Go to 4
Winter browning or frosting is caused by water stress in late
winter and usually affects heather on exposed ground (see
4.7). This sometimes occurs in conjunction with heavy grazing which can expose the plants and accentuate the damage.

48

4. *Are there thin black flattened horse hair like strands attached to stems?*

No = Look more carefully, or do you think it could be weather or fire induced?

Yes = Probably the heather rhizomorph fungus. Small toadstools may be seen on stems or amongst the litter during the summer, with small caps and depressed in the middle. Often occurs in damp conditions and may not have caused the damage; more likely a secondary infection as a result of water stress through grazing.

5. *Are some shoots remaining but the foliage is partially eaten with distinct bites?*

No = Go to 9
Yes = Go to 6

6. *Does the heather show distinct growth forms shown on page 29?*

No = Go to 7
Yes = You are looking at heavy grazing by sheep or deer. You should refer back to Chapter 3.

7. *Are the shoots cleanly snipped?*

No = Go to 8
Yes = Shoots often eaten at an oblique angle with some runways would suggest hare or rabbit damage. Inspect around the heather for rabbit and hare dropping and for footprints. Rabbit/hare control may be necessary (see Chapter 9).

8. *Have the shoots and foliage been partly eaten and even parts of the leaves eaten?*

No = Are you sure that part of the plant has been eaten?
Yes = Possibly eaten by a large caterpillar such as emperor moth, northern eggar moth, fox moth, vapourer moth, magpie moth or winter moth (Action see 4.6). Most of the common species hatch and feed earlier than heather beetle and cause browning in late May or early June rather than late July and August.

**9.** *Are leaves and shoots eaten but this is not clear with the naked eye?*

Yes = Probably a heather beetle attack. Bark on shoots may also be stripped and the leaves forming an orange-reddish colour before going grey and dying. Usually on flat boggy ground below 300m. Adults may be present or larvae seen amongst roots (see 4.4).

**10.** *The plant is not consumed, although there may be a die back of shoots and foliage colour. Have the plants been squashed and flattened against the ground?*

No = Go to 12

Yes = Could be caused by snow mould. The leaves should change from a green to brown to grey colour before dying. There should also be a fine cobweb-like strands amongst the foliage and shoots in areas where snow has recently melted. No real solution to this problem but this should not cause any serious loss of heather. Alternatively trampling damage caused by walkers, vehicles or stock. This tends to occur on and around tracks and should be associated with a bruising and breakage of stems.

**11.** *Plants on exposed ground not flattened against the ground, as if snow has laid on them.*

No = Go to 12

Yes = Probably winter browning or some other form of weather induced water stress, perhaps because the ground has been frozen or the plants exposed to high winds. The leaves frequently turn from green to a purplish brown colour over 3 to 20 days. Occurs on exposed areas where snow may have blown clear.

**12.** Plants could be suffering from heather rhizomorph fungus (see 4 above) or root damage by one of the weevils (4.5). Usually vegetation turns from green to brown over varying periods. Examine the stems for the signs of the beetle.

*This key was adapted from a key by Angus MacDonald (Heather damage: a guide to types of damage and their causes: 2nd edition. Research and Survey in Nature Conservation, JNCC Peterborough). Special thanks to Angus and colleagues at SNH.*

## 4.3  Heather beetle life cycle

- Adult beetles emerge from winter hibernation on warm days in April and May and even though they are poor fliers they may appear in swarms. Adults are not usually active between July and October.

- Eggs are laid in May and June in damp heather litter or amongst *Sphagnum* moss and the characteristic larvae emerge and are active from June through to mid-August, feeding on the young heather shoots. Careful examination of the plant at this stage may reveal

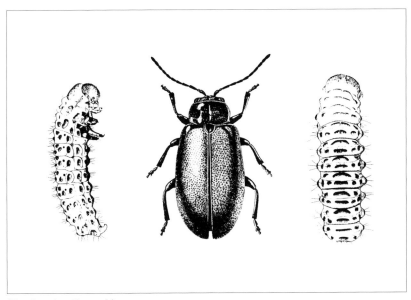

Heather beetle and larvae

leaves with jagged edges and areas of bark that have been shaved away. The larvae are difficult to see on the plants but pulling the heather up often reveals the larvae around the base of the plant.

- Damage of the heather can be severe and results in a reddish or orange-brown colour in August, after which the plant turns grey and dies during the autumn.

- By mid-August the larvae are starting to pupate (white maggots) around the base of the plant. These emerge as adults in September and then fly off to hibernate for the winter.

## 4.4 Identifying heather beetle damage and the solution

- Most heather damage is not noticed until August when the heather turns orange-brown. By this time most of the damage has been done and the larvae have pupated. *Burning at this stage is illegal and would probably not be beneficial.*

- Heather damage often appears severe but young heather plants recover well by producing new shoots from dormant buds. The best course of action is usually do nothing.

- Heather attack may occur over a series of years which can kill even young plants. In such instances burning parts of the afflicted areas should result in recovery of heather from seed or where possible root stock.

- Severely damaged old heather may need to be burnt and can recover from heather seed. Young heather, unless completely dead, should recover and should not be burnt.

- Worst attacks are on wet boggy ground where burning may not be possible. Heather beetles in such areas are often followed by a parasitoid wasp which parasitizes and kills the beetle larvae.

## 4.5 Winter moth and other caterpillars

• Caterpillar attacks on heather can be dramatic with in excess of 1500 caterpillars per square metre. The damage is obvious and can become extensive although the best management strategy is often to wait for the epidemic to pass and concentrate on repairing the damage. A number of moths can cause the damage although the species are fairly similar in behaviour and life cycle. Much of what follows concentrates on the more common winter moth.

• The winter moth has caused dramatic damage to areas of heather moorland and was particularly active in parts of Scotland during 1992 and 1993. The moth is traditionally a pest of broad-leaved trees such as oak, birch and apple although it now attacks spruce plantations.

• The larvae hatch in mid-April and the caterpillars cause much of the heather damage between April and June. The caterpillars are light green with a dark yellow stripe down the back and two lighter stripes down the side.

• Caterpillars frequently eat the blaeberry first and switch to heather as the blaeberry is eaten out.

• The outbreak is often restricted to begin with but spreads down-wind with time as the young caterpillars produce fine silken threads which enable them to "balloon" in the wind to fresh heather areas. As a consequence of this behaviour new outbreaks usually occur on exposed areas of heather.

• Larvae pupate in the soil and do not emerge as adults until November – December when the pale brown males can be seen fluttering around the top of the heather in the late afternoon on a relatively mild dry day.

- Females are flightless, mate on the heather and then lay their eggs in the heather plant or amongst the ground litter.

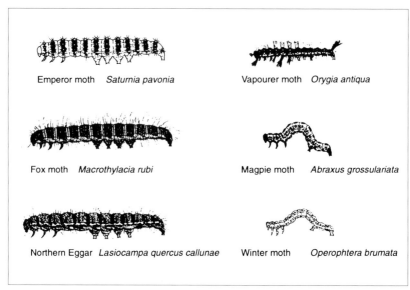

Emperor moth   *Saturnia pavonia*

Vapourer moth   *Orygia antiqua*

Fox moth   *Macrothylacia rubi*

Magpie moth   *Abraxus grossulariata*

Northern Eggar  *Lasiocampa quercus callunae*

Winter moth   *Operophtera brumata*

*Larvae of six moths which can cause damage to heather.*
(With thanks to Angus MacDonald/SNH.)

## 4.6  Control of winter moth

- Winter moth outbreaks usually occur in old heavily grazed heather and the best strategy is to burn the heather during the correct time of the year (Chapter 2) and remove grazing animals – probably until the following spring.

- Caterpillar outbreaks are usually epidemics that die back after a year or two, probably because of viral infections, although there is some evidence that harsh winters may help to control the moth since adults cannot emerge when the ground is frozen.

- Large scale application of insecticides will not guarantee a successful result, will probably be expensive, illegal and may reduce other insects eaten by grouse.

- Potential outbreaks can be controlled in spring with fire although a back fire is probably needed to reach a high temperature and kill most of the egg masses. This may prove difficult in areas of rank heather where the heather has opened up.

*Special thanks to Susan Hartley, ITE, Banchory for information on winter moths.*

## 4.7 Winter browning of heather

- Winter browning describes the condition of heather when it turns reddish brown in winter and dies.

- Winter browning is not caused by low temperatures but by low humidity, often associated with cold dry winds, which results in water stress and death of the plant.

- Winter browning is sometimes called frosting since it occurs after periods of severe frost although the frost may act with insect and fungal attack.

- Winter browning tends to occur on the windward side of heather edges.

- Damage by insects such as heather beetles is similar to frosting since the beetles prevent the plant from obtaining water. However, insect damage is usually obvious during the summer months and winter browning occurs in late winter before the end of April when the heather starts growing. Moreover insect attack show signs of damage on stems, leaves or roots.

- Badly frosted heather should be burnt to encourage regeneration from seed but lightly frosted heather will recover.

- Snow cover provides protection from winter browning although when snow blows clear the exposed heather may then suffer.

# CHAPTER FIVE

# Bracken Control

Bracken has been described as the scourge of Scotland and the plague of western Britain. Bracken replaces productive heather dominant moorland with a weed which is toxic to grazing animals, provides a good habitat for ticks and generally reduces the capital value of land. We consider here the means for reducing the effects of bracken.

## 5.1 The biology of bracken

• Bracken is the most widespread vascular plant in the world; an opportunistic weed that is currently increasing in Britain at a rate of 3% per annum.

• Bracken is remarkably successful because it is tolerant of a wide range of climatic conditions, it is unpalatable, resistant to disease, can withstand burning, inhibits the growth of other species by releasing allelopathic compounds into the soil and has a highly developed rhizome system which allows it to spread rapidly.

• Bracken is of low conservation value, only 15 species of bird breed in bracken beds while 33 breed on the heather it replaces. There are no specialist birds that live in bracken alone although it provides good cover for some species like the whinchat and twite.

• Bracken is highly toxic when consumed and can cause blindness in some herbivores and cancer in ruminants.

- Bracken was once a prized resource, cut by farmers as bedding for over-wintering livestock but since bracken is no longer controlled through this technique it has spread dramatically.

- Bracken is favoured as a consequence of poor burning practices and in some circumstances by localised grazing pressure.

- For the future, bracken could be used as a biofuel. This is both technically feasible and close to financial viability but the idea still requires to be tested commercially.

## 5.2 Planning to control bracken

- Define the area of bracken to be treated as the area in which good regeneration of other vegetation is possible.

- Examine what is under the bracken, if it is a thick layer of bracken mat then vegetation restoration would be difficult without intensive physical follow up treatment.

- Some areas of bracken may not regenerate easily, they can remain sterile for in excess of 10 years and may lead to erosion unless the ground can be stabilised with nurse grasses.

- Map areas where bracken is encroaching into good heather ground and tackle these as a priority. Small areas can be sprayed through ground application.

- Map areas where bracken beds are thick with a deep mat layer and areas where follow up treatment would be difficult. These are areas of low priority.

- Map areas of bracken which can be removed by physical means or ground spraying as opposed to areas where helicopter treatment is required. These should be treated first before the main problem areas are tackled with helicopters.

- Determine the area of bracken ground suitable for aerial spraying and then organise a phased programme of bracken spraying to ensure that all areas sprayed receive subsequent after-care.

- The biggest limitation with bracken spraying is suitable follow up treatment. The treatable area depends on the availability of labour in following years and the type of ground. One person with equipment should be able to cope with 100 hectares (250 acres) each year following good aerial spraying.

## 5.3 Spraying bracken – basic principles

- The most effective technique at the current time for controlling bracken is through spraying with the herbicide Asulox (Rhône Poulenc).

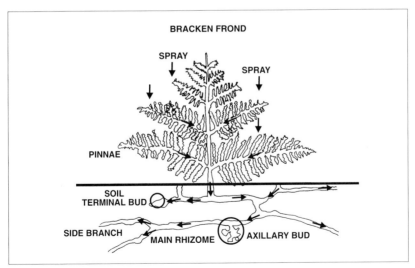

*The structure of bracken, showing the transportation of Asulox to the underground rhizomes.*

- Using the correct approach, Asulox spraying will kill about 95% of bracken. Nevertheless, *the essential part of bracken control is the follow up treatment.* If effective follow up techniques are not undertaken the remaining 5% will spread and the advantages of the first spraying will be lost.

- Asulox is a herbicide which is absorbed by the fronds and translocated by the plant down to the underground rhizomes and buds that would have developed in the following season. After treatment, the bracken dies back naturally but there is no new growth from the buds in the following year.

- The time of spraying is crucial. Bracken should be sprayed when the fronds have just reached their full frond stage and are still soft to the touch. Spraying is usually between mid July and early August.

- Before you start, calculate accurately the area to spray. Mark the area to be sprayed with canes and easily visible red streamers.

- Measure the area to be sprayed accurately, directly on the ground with steps or by using the milometer on a 4WD bike. Do not estimate from a map, this can seriously underestimate the area of sloping ground (a hillside at 45° angle has 38% more area than shown on a map). Failure to get this correct may lead to poor spraying and lack of grant aid.

- Do not spray when the fronds are still emerging or when the fronds have started to die back.

- Do not spray when the fronds have been hardened by drought or damaged by late frost with more than 10% of the surface area damaged.

- Spray on a dry day when rainfall is not expected for at least 24 hours. With most techniques there should be little wind, although for drift spraying a gentle breeze is needed.

- Rainfall within 24 hours of spraying will reduce the efficiency of control but relatively high humidity can improve uptake of Asulox.

## 5.4 Aerial application of Asulox

- Aerial application in the uplands is best undertaken with a helicopter and requires a skilled and sensible contractor.

- The advantages of aerial application include speed and access to difficult terrain.

- The disadvantage of aerial application include spraying an area too large for follow up treatment and the difficulty of obtaining good control under trees, outcrops and gullies or on ground where the slope is more than 60%.

- The aerial contractor must ensure that the terrain is suitable and be prepared only to fly when rain is not expected for 24 hours.

- Accurate and obvious ground marking is essential to ensure no over-lapping or missed areas. Fixed wing craft have more problems here because of faster flying speeds.

- Produce detailed maps for the contractor showing the area to be sprayed. Maps must also mark all tall buildings, pylons, houses, crags, trees, overhead cables and telephone wires, nature reserves, Sites of Special Scientific Interest, bee hives etc. within a one mile distance around the area.

- Aircraft should fly 2m to 3m (6 to 10ft) above the bracken canopy. In broken ground with changing gradients and streams this may be difficult to achieve and unless more than 75% can be

*Aerial spraying of Asulox is best done by helicopter.*

sprayed at a height of less than 5m (15ft) it is not worth spraying from an aircraft.

- Pilots should take care about aerial drift and should not fly when wind speeds exceed 10 knots.

- Pilots should avoid spray drift outside the sprayed area and uneven application as a consequence of cross winds.

- Given the ground conditions, determine with the contractor the acceptable rate of kill before treatment and the conditions for re-spraying if this is not achieved.

- Asulox should be applied at 11.2 litres of Asulox in 44 litres of water per hectare (8 pints in 4 gallons of water per acre), incorporating a proprietary wetting agent. Higher volumes up to 77 litres per hectare will generally give better results.

- Colour dyes mixed with the Asulox can show areas not correctly treated.

## 5.5 Ground application

- A range of hand held motorised applicators, tractor-mounted or bike-mounted crop sprayers can provide a suitable method of applying Asulox.

- For ground application Asulox should be mixed at the rate of 11.2 litres per hectare (8 pints per acre) in a volume of water appropriate for the equipment used.

- Weed wipes are used both for initial control and follow up treatment. A tractor-mounted weed wipe can be effective on rocky ground or in areas where water is hard to obtain.

- Hand held weed wipes are easy to use and fairly light but labour intensive and only really suitable for small and difficult areas or follow up treatment (See 5.7).

- Ultra Low Volume Applicators (ULVA) are an effective application technique to control bracken stands of 0.3-2ha (1-5 acres) in size. These machines work by gravity feed onto a rotary atomiser which produces uniformly correct size droplets wafted on the breeze across the bracken beds.

- Many of these ULVAS operate from battery power and are fed from a 1 litre bottle.

- Plan the route through the bracken bed before starting. Mark with pegs or flags routes across the wind at 4 to 5m apart. Walk through the bracken slowly and allow the ULVA to deliver the spray over an area of 5 or more metres. Repeat the transects at 5m intervals to ensure good coverage.

- Use in light wind conditions where the wind is 3-8 kph (2-5 mph).

- Ensure batteries are fully charged before starting for the hill and carry spares. Clean the ULVA out after use with water and soap mixture.

## 5.6 Physical control of bracken

- Rolling crushing or cutting bracken can be an effective method of control. The basic principle is to break and crush the bracken until it is effectively exhausted.

- Bracken should be cut or crushed when the fronds have been above ground for about 2-3 weeks and the tractor operator can easily avoid obstacles. Ideally this should be repeated in late July with follow up treatment in following years.

- Ideal ground for crushing is fairly flat with few rocks. Steep sides are not possible.

- Rolling or crushing techniques should aim to break the stalks of the bracken as it is growing. This may mean rolling in one direction and rolling again in the opposite direction.

- Crushers are usually constructed from gang rollers or chains. Rollers are often four sided and joined to a heavy metal bar and towed behind a tractor.

- In England, some National Parks (e.g. North York Moors) and other conservation organisations may own crushers which are let out free of charge for bracken control.

- In areas with a thick mat layer, physical treatment can help to break and dry the mat, allowing other vegetation to colonise.

## 5.7 Bracken follow up treatment

- The importance of after-care cannot be stressed too strongly. Any surviving patches of undamaged bracken must be treated in the following years.

- Bracken which shows signs of damage or distortion such as stunting or yellowing will not respond to spraying and is best removed through physical actions such as hand pulling or cutting.

- Many of the ground application techniques can be used as follow up treatment depending on available labour and equipment.

- Sprayers mounted on the back of 4WD bikes can make spraying efficient; some have 30m extension hoses.

- Knapsack spot spraying can be an effective way of controlling isolated fronds. Asulox should be applied as 1 part Asulox to 100 parts water. For a 5 litre sprayer use 50ml (for 1 gallon use 1.5 fluid ounces of Asulox).

- Weed wipes can be effective, particularly when used on a boom or similar device mounted on the back of a 4WD bike, ATV or tractor.

- Hand held weed wipes can be used in follow up treatment. These look like a brush, hold chemical within the handle and have a wick at the end. Asulox should be applied with a wetting agent at the rate of 11 parts Asulox to 7 parts wetting agent. Roundup can also be used at the rate of 1 part Roundup to 50 parts water.

- Hand held weed wipes are light and easy to use on steep ground. They do not usually require refilling during a day and so are useful when used away from water.

- Hand cutting and pulling can be a quick and straight forward technique when labour is available or there are relatively few fronds remaining. As a general rule, pull or remove all fronds when you are walking or passing through an area where bracken was controlled in previous years.

## 5.8 Grant aid for bracken spraying

- A grant of up to 30% of the approved costs of bracken control and follow up treatment is available under the Farm and Conservation Grant Scheme.

- Farmers in some Environmentally Sensitive Areas (ESAs) may obtain financial assistance for bracken control.

- Obtain advice before spraying from Game Conservancy Ltd's Advisory Service, MAFF, SOAFD or WOAD on how to apply for grant aid.

- The site may have to be surveyed and the grant making body may stipulate pre- or post-care treatment.

- Grant aid will not usually be paid until after-care treatment has been carried out.

- Grant aid used to rely on follow up which included lime and slagging but this has been changed, and any follow up which leads to replacement with suitable feed for sheep, including heather and blaeberry is now acceptable.

## 5.9  Dos and Don'ts of bracken control

- **Do** plan the operation to account for where heather vegetation will recover fast

- **Do** measure the area to be sprayed on the ground and not on a map

- **Do** spray on dry calm days when rainfall is not expected for 24 hours

- **Do** spray only undamaged fronds

- **Do** ensure aerial spraying is safe and not at a height greater than 3m (15ft)

- **Do** read and comply with on label approvals and ensure all who apply the herbicide are qualified

- **Do not** cut or crush bracken that has been sprayed within the past 21 days

- **Do not** spray an area so large that effective follow up treatment would not be possible

- **Do not** spray close to water courses or water catchment areas

CHAPTER SIX

# Grass Control

All moorland areas have grasses, rushes and sedges growing in combination with the heather and bilberry. Some species are beneficial to grouse, sheep and deer by providing food at certain times of the year. Others are aggressive, invasive species which can dominate the heather moorland. Being able to identify a small number of the key species enables the moorland manager to make informed decisions regarding the management of the moor.

## 6.1 Grazing and grasses

• Sheep prefer to graze grass species during the summer months since these tend to be more nutritious than heather. They only switch to the evergreen heather and other shrubs when the grasses have died back during the autumn.

• Having a balanced grass heather mix on the moor can help sustain multiple land use and the recycling of nutrients. An imbalance with too much grass leads to fewer grouse.

• Some species are aggressive, unpalatable grasses. Since these species are not favoured by the sheep and deer they tend to invade grazed or recently disturbed areas. They also tend to form a thick mat and provide a suitable habitat for ticks.

• Some of these aggressive species also spread into areas of recently burnt heather, out-competing the heather and replacing it with a sward of little value to sheep or grouse.

# BENEFICIAL SPECIES

## 6.2 Cotton grass *Eriophorum vaginatum*

- A common species found growing in conjunction with heather on the wetter blanket bog moorland. It is a native perennial which grows in tussocks, spreading by means of rhizomes.

Cotton grass

- This cotton grass is a very characteristic species, distinguished from the other British cotton grass by having a single flower on each spike.

- The immature flower heads which occur from February to April provide an important source of nutrients to grouse and other moorland herbivores before the heather starts growing, and they will grow under the snow.

- Common names include draw moss, moss crop, or just moss.

- While cotton grass increases with grazing pressure, over-utilisation of the flower heads by sheep reduces the availability of the immature flower heads for grouse.

## 6.3 Wavy hair-grass *Deschampsia flexuosa*

- A common species on peaty soils and usually an early coloniser after fires where the grass is present in association with heather.

- A native perennial forming tall tufts, spreading by seed and rhizomes. The flower head branches are strongly wavy. Flowers from June to July.

- As an early coloniser, wavy hairgrass forms a cover over the bare soil, reducing the risk of erosion and protecting heather seedlings as they first emerge. Heather out-dominates the grass in time with moderate grazing and it is generally not a problem for moorland management.

Wavy hair-grass

- A palatable species for sheep and deer, it may become a problem when grazing animals over-utilise the heather.

### 6.4 Sheep's fescue *Festuca ovina*

- Common throughout moorland in upland Britain. A native perennial which forms thick tufts.

- An important component of sheep diet being relatively palatable, flowers from May to July, height 5 to 60cm.

Sheep's fescue

70

## 6.5 Deer grass *Trichophorum cespitosum*

- A common species in wet boggy areas in upland Britain, a native perennial, forming dense tufts. The upper leaf sheath is prolonged into a short bristle-like blade which is useful for recognising the species.

- Height 5 to 25cm, flowers May to June.

- A palatable species for sheep and deer grazing.

Deer grass

## DETRIMENTAL SPECIES

## 6.6 Purple moor-grass *Molinia caerulea*

- A common species on the wetter moorland areas of upland Britain, where it often dominates, forming vast areas of tufts and tussocks.

- *Molinia* grows well and dominates where water is moving through the soil. When the water stagnates or the soil is prone to droughts the *Molinia* is much weaker and does not form into tussocks.

Molinia

- A native perennial, but is deciduous, with the straw-like leaves dying off through the autumn and winter. This habit gives rise to one of its common names, 'blow grass', as the dead leaf blows away in the winter months.

- The flower head is usually dark purple, the height is 15 to 120cm with flowers from July to September.

- The grass has a low palatability for most of the year but with a short flush between June and August when cattle and other grazing animals will eat it.

- Purple moor-grass forms a major problem when it occurs in the sward along with heather. If the purple moor-grass/heather mix is burnt, the fast growing competitive grass out-competes the heather and dominates the sward.

- *Do not burn areas with purple moor-grass/heather mixes.*

- Purple moor-grass benefits from burning and forms large stands of poor quality vegetation.

- Control techniques are expensive and time consuming, however a number of options do exist.

- **Control:** The use of a selective herbicide which kills the grass and does not affect the heather in the sward is one possible approach and could allow the heather to compete for dominance of the sward. Previously the chemical DALAPON was used but this has been removed from the market, meanwhile other chemicals are being tested.

- **Control:** In pure stands of purple moor-grass, complete destruction of the grass can be attempted by removing the leaf growth 2 or 3 times per annum with a heavy duty rotary slasher. This should deplete the plant's reserves and should, over 2 or 3 years, destroy the purple moor-grass.

- **Control:** In pure stands of purple moor-grass the leaf growth can be removed chemically by spraying with a Glyphosate, this again will exhaust the plant and lead to die back. Repeated treatment may be necessary in the following year.

- **Control:** Intensive grazing can be used to control purple moor-grass. Cattle will graze the grass hard for a short period in July but this approach is often logistically impossible and may be compromised by cattle poaching wet ground.

- **Control:** A second approach is to use primitive breeds of sheep to graze the purple moor-grass since research has shown that some breeds will take sufficient quantities of the grass during the summer to deplete the reserves of the plant. For further advice and guidance contact Game Conservancy Ltd's Advisors.

### 6.7 Mat grass *Nardus stricta*

- Mat grass dominates the drier areas of moorland in much of upland Britain. The species is unpalatable to sheep due to high levels of silicates in the leaves, making the plant tough and fibrous.

- Mat grass is a native perennial which forms dense tufts. Small hard tufts are often found uprooted and discarded. Its height is 10 to 40cm, flowering June to August.

Mat grass

- Great care needs to be taken when burning near mat grass and heather mixes as the stand can regenerate to an all mat grass sward. However with reduced grazing and infrequent fires, the heather should once again be able to out-compete the mat grass.

- **Control:** Control is difficult. Glyphosate sprays can be used on dense, even stands of mat grass. Cattle will graze the grass very early in the growing season, but the benefits gained from grazing may be lost if heather and other species are trampled. Reduced grazing and time may slowly help heather to dominate.

### 6.8 Heath rush *Juncus squarrosus*

- A common species on the acid soils of moors and heaths, especially where sheep grazing is heavy. In general, a good indicator of high grazing pressure.

Heath rush

- Heath rush is a native perennial forming dense tufts easily recognised by the rosette of leaves strongly bent back against the ground and the straight tough flowering stem in the centre. Height is 15 to 50cm; flowers from June to July.

- The seed heads are eaten by grouse in the late summer/early autumn and their attraction may result in temporary disappearance of large numbers of grouse during the shooting season. Overall this species is probably of little significance as a food plant for grouse.

- No effective form of control is currently known.

## 6.9 Soft rush *Juncus effusus*

- A native perennial which can form thick tufts, very common in boggy moorland areas throughout Britain. Has a smooth light yellowish green stem with the flowers two thirds of the way to the top. Height is 30 to 150cm, flowering June to August.

- Soft rush can form into large beds and choke productive flush areas. As a rule it indicates good feeding ground for grouse chicks but such areas can dry out and consequently reduce insect productivity.

Soft rush

- **Control:** Glyphosate may be useful on large beds.

- **Control:** Repeated cutting possibly in conjunction with grazing will suppress the growth rate, however access to the site with a wheeled vehicle may be difficult due to its boggy nature.

# CHAPTER SEVEN

# The Control of Fox Predation

Given suitable habitat, the control of fox predation is the most essential element in producing a harvestable surplus of grouse. The first rule of grouse management is to have a suitable number of active keepers who control fox numbers throughout the year. The second rule is to ensure a similar strategy occurs on neighbouring ground. Remember, however, that good game managers and sportsmen should not want to exterminate every last fox in the country.

## 7.1 Foxes and fox predation

• Numbers of foxes in upland Britain have increased dramatically this century. Foxes were extinct at the turn of the century in various parts of upland Britain and have increased rapidly since the Second World War and in line with the decline in keeper numbers and the increase in rabbits after myxomatosis, particularly between 1961 and 1977.

• Fox control is one of the most important aspects of grouse production and should be the major task of the keeper throughout the year. Fox control is not cheap and when you consider the time and costs of a keeper, each adult fox dead may well cost more than £2000, but the benefits in grouse production can be equally large.

• Probably the largest impact foxes have on grouse is during the breeding season when foxes will take incubating hens and whole broods of chicks. Nevertheless, many underestimate the effects of foxes during the winter months. It is essential to undertake fox control throughout the year.

- Foxes live in family groups which share territories. The size of these territories may be as large as 4000ha (7000 acres) in uplands where food availability is poor.

- Foxes disperse during autumn and winter and many estates experience an influx of young foxes at this time. Some males travel 50km (30 miles) within a night. Few boundaries will stop a fox dispersing; rivers and lochs can be swum.

- Mating usually takes place in late December and January with cubs being born 53 days later in March and April.

- Litter sizes are usually 4-5 cubs. The vixen stays with the cubs until these are 3 weeks of age and then joins the dog fox in feeding the cubs.

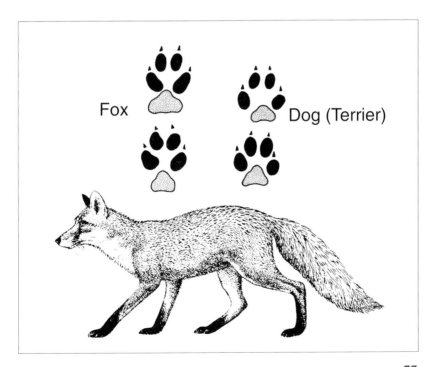

## 7.2 Signs of foxes and fox predation

- Foxes kill adult and young grouse and will take eggs.

- A characteristic fox kill will have most of the carcass missing but leave the wings and a large part of the guts chopped up. The primary feathers may be left, bitten off close to their base.

- Rabbits and other mammals are often bitten in half and the carcass broken up.

- Fox predation on grouse during the summer may be noted by a loss of hen grouse taken from the nest and this can be detected by comparing the spring and July counts. The ratio of hens to cocks in the July count will be biased more towards cocks than hens when foxes and sometimes stoats take a large number of incubating hens. Low density grouse populations often have a large surplus of cocks, even in spring.

- Fox markings are clear in sand, mud and snow. Compared with dog tracks, fox footings are more oval, almost pointed. Like dogs, foxes show only four toes when they walk but because they often place their hind foot in the slot of the front foot, the tracks may appear to have five toes. Badgers show five toes.

- In snow, fox marks can be very clear, usually trotting, often in a distinctly straight line. A walking fox does not produce such a straight course.

- Foxes can be heard calling – yapping, barking, screaming and sometimes wailing – and are particularly vocal during the mating season and may even be heard during the middle of the day.

- Dens should be located, usually from the local knowledge of experienced keepers and shepherds. Prior to the breeding season dens are cleaned out and signs of fresh earth and fox smell will indicate use. An occupied den is obvious by the unconsumed food remains inside the entrance. As a rule, dens are only used during breeding or by the occasional passing fox unless weather conditions are harsh.

- Dens should be left quiet. Frequently disturbed dens result in foxes cubbing elsewhere.

- Fox droppings or scats are variable in colour, being brown – almost black when fresh, and grey to white when dried out. Droppings are pointed, with fur, wool, feather, bone fragments and the remains of beetles evident. They are frequently left on stones or prominent objects. Foxes use urine to mark – a characteristic strong smell easily noticed by most people.

- Look for signs of foxes under fences where fox fur may snag.

- In some parts of the country, particularly the Scottish Borders, areas of rough grass can carry large numbers of voles and signs of scratching, or of the fox's muzzle being pushed into the grass whilst sniffing out voles are common. Dead voles (and moles) are frequently left on the surface.

- A characteristic habit of foxes is the caching of food. A partly eaten grouse, perhaps with leg and feet protruding, will be buried in a peaty patch and be noted by terriers or other dogs.

## 7.3 Planning fox control

- The essence of good fox control is to tackle the foxes with a wide range of techniques. A fox that may be lamp-shy might be snared and one that has avoided snares may be caught in a kist (7.11). The full range of techniques described below is essential.

- Foxes kill grouse throughout the year, so do not leave fox control until the spring. Do not feel that three weeks 'doing the dens' will suffice. Fox control means winter nights lamping, spring nights lying out close to a den, and checking snares and middens day in and day out throughout the winter.

- Keep a map of the estate and surrounding areas and mark on it the location of all traps, regular lamping routes and dens. Each time a fox is seen and a fox is killed mark on the map where this occurred. Such information will show clearly the routes used by foxes entering an estate and help concentrate the mind on both the best combination of techniques and an understanding of the foxes.

- Note the location of neighbouring forestry blocks and plan to snare along the edges (7.4). Talk to locals and determine whether you could join the local hound club and have them visit any small forestry plantations (7.7).

- Note all suitable areas for lamping and plan a lamping campaign during the winter (7.6).

- There are a large number of fox destruction societies around Britain, these often consist of a group of farmers and exist in areas where there are few keepers available to control foxes.

- Note that the control of fox predation does not include only lethal techniques but also non-lethal techniques such as the removal of alternative prey species, particularly rabbits and all carrion including, dead sheep, deer grallochs and possible food sources from human waste and rubbish.

- Forestry ground is generally considered a poor neighbour as far as fox control is concerned, particularly since most private forestry owners undertake little fox control and The Forestry Authority have now stopped snaring inside plantations and only allow shooting.

- Consider the needs of local packs of foxhounds.

## 7.4  Fox snaring

- Careful snaring can be a highly effective technique for reducing a fox population and if undertaken properly can be both efficient and humane. In the uplands this is one of the most effective techniques for reducing fox numbers and is a fundamental technique of the moorland keeper.

- The important points about snaring are to set the snare in a manner that will not catch non-target species (roe deer, sheep, badgers etc.). It is a requirement of law to ensure that all snares are checked at least every 24 hours and that snared foxes are despatched humanely.

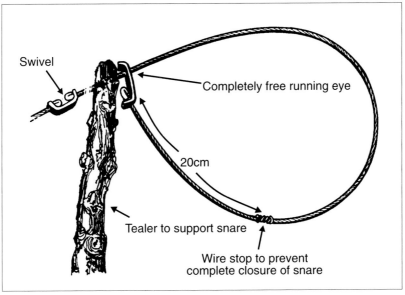

Swivel

Completely free running eye

20cm

Tealer to support snare

Wire stop to prevent
complete closure of snare

*A correctly set fox snare.*

- Snares can be bought from a country shop or from Game Conservancy Ltd. Many keepers still make their own and work hard to ensure all wire and snares are carefully weathered before use, to reduce associated smells of oil and man.

- Newly made snares should be degreased by boiling in water and washing-up liquid and skimming off all scum. They can be tanned by boiling in tea and rubbing with earth. Some keepers will spray with green paint while others will rub beeswax in to ensure clean running in cold conditions.

- Snares should be constructed of strong wire that will not break and cannot be chewed through by a fox. The wire must not be springy, or the snare may open and allow a fox to escape. Self-locking snares are illegal.

- Stops should be fitted about 20cm from the eye to prevent the snare from closing to less than 6cm in diameter. The idea of this is to allow a deer or sheep that may get tangled by the feet to escape. Many commercial snares leave the stop free for the user to fit. If this is the case then place the snare on an anvil and hit the stop firmly with a hammer.

- A good technique with modern snares is to kink the wire slightly where the loop of the set snare normally starts. This will prevent the loop accidentally opening when the fox first enters, causing the animal to escape or to be caught around the chest or waist.

- A swivel should be attached between the loop and the tether. The eye of the snare should be made with a metal loop or ring.

- Snares must be set away from areas where they are likely to catch non-target species or cause offence to other users of the country-side; shepherds, hikers or others. Keep them well away from foot-paths.

- The standard snare should be set about 20cm above ground with a 15cm loop supported by a tealer, usually of wood but care should be taken to ensure this blends in with the vegetation.

- Snares must be secured, usually to a strong wooden stob or a 40cm length of angle iron knocked down to ground level. In woodland, a heavy drag is an alternative.

- As a rule snares are usually set along hill tracks. Other helpful sites may be near openings in forestry fences, alongside streams or in other fox runs noted during snowy conditions.

- Snares should never be set actually in a hole in a fence as this carries a high risk of non-target captures.

- Each keeper should be running as many snares as he can visit daily.

## 7.5  Snares and middens

- Snares can be set in areas where sheep and other animals are on the hill but only with great care. Many upland keepers ease the burden of daily checking and increase efficiency by using middens.

- Middens are basically areas of buried, smelly bait, usually carcasses, which attract foxes. Foxes approaching the carcasses along paths get caught in snares.

- By law, all dead animals used must be buried. The bait can include dead sheep, deer grallochs, fish offal or anything suitable. Freshen the midden with new bait every two weeks.

- If there is a danger of catching non-target species, such as farm livestock, it may be necessary to surround the midden with a roll of 50-100m of mesh fencing but with holes and gaps around the base for the foxes to slip under. Select old fencing wire and posts.

- From each of the obvious approaches a 20cm wide path is cut with a strimmer to lead the foxes towards the midden. Inside the midden each path is carefully snared with half a dozen snares. If the midden is fenced then cut a path around the outside so the fox can find the necessary openings. Do not snare in the gaps in the fence.

- Middens should be sited close to fox runs but not on them. Good sites are close to the junction of two streams or at the base of a hill where foxes are known to run.

- The middens need to be sited in dense vegetation and some of the most successful places are in deep rushes or young forestry.

- Remember that snares in middens have to be checked every 24 hours like any other snare, so place them in areas where you can readily visit them. Each keeper should aim to run about five middens.


## 7.6  Fox lamping

- The lamping of foxes at night with a strong quartz halogen lamp and shooting with a good rifle has proved one of the most effective and efficient methods of fox control in the uplands. This is well illustrated by the insignia of most modern day keepers – a 4WD vehicle with a spot light mounted on the cab.

- Effective lamping requires good access routes to the hill that can be driven safely at night. Ideally these hill roads should permit the keeper to lamp from his vehicle into all corries and areas where foxes can be controlled. A route around the estate march will allow a keeper to keep the central part of the hill clear of foxes.

- Sensitively placed hill roads which are not an eye-sore are an advantage to the modern keeper as long as they do not open up wilderness areas.

- Most keepers lamp using their 4WD vehicle and will then shoot a sighted fox across the bonnet of the vehicle. Some keepers now use 4WD bikes with a bar across the handlebars positioned to allow a good rest. In these instances the keeper may mount a lamp on a helmet, slightly offset so that when siting a fox with the gun, the lamp is pointing directly forward in the line of view.

- Biking routes should be carefully worked out during light hours and care taken to keep to these to avoid damaging wet boggy areas.

- Safety is paramount throughout. Far better not to fire at a fox than risk an accident. Learn the ground well before foxing an area so the person who fires the rifle knows the location of all houses and roads.

- The basic approach is to drive the hill roads slowly, scanning the lamp across the side of the hill and looking for the eye shine of a fox. When sighted at an angle, foxes usually show a pair of red eyes but blue/white eyes or even green eyes when seen head on. They have a characteristic gait, occasionally running and then turning back towards the lamp. The eyes of a cat can look like fox eyes but tend to be greener. *Never just shoot at a pair of eyes – positively identify the animal first.*

- Once spotted, the lamp should play on the fox but using only the lower part of the beam. It is important the fox is unaware that you are there so nothing like a wing mirror or rifle should cross the beam.

- Foxes can be called in with a rabbit squeaker. Most people can do this with the back of their hand although a small mouth squeaker leaves the hands free to work the rifle or lamp. Commercial squeakers are available or a piece of polystyrene scraped against the windscreen can do the job. Squeak three times then leave for 3 minutes and then lamp the ground. If a fox is sighted squeak again, but not too much.

- Foxes can also be called using a portable tape recorder with a recording of a fox. A recording of a vixen calling will attract a male in the autumn and a cub squealing will pull foxes during the spring but be careful as they may be moving fast towards you. Do carry a shotgun as well as a rifle at all times when lamping; foxes can come too close for the safe use of a rifle.

- Foxes can become lamp-shy, running away fast once the light comes to rest on them. This is usually because they have been shot at and missed; such foxes are difficult to shoot on the lamp and usually have to be killed by another technique.

### 7.7 Fox driving and hounds

- There are a number of excellent packs of fox hounds in the uplands of Britain which carry out fox control as an efficient and effective technique. These hounds, many of them 'gun packs', are principally there for fox control, not sport. In many instances these packs can flush foxes from dense conifer plantations and other areas of ground that a keeper would have trouble in reaching.

- In general, hounds are successful in blocks of forestry up to 40ha (100 acres) in size. Larger blocks are more difficult to handle, although parts of larger blocks can be subdivided with men equipped with shotguns in the rides. In some areas packs are used in large forestry blocks to chase the fox to ground, then allowing the hunters to dig the fox out and to know where den is located.

- Hounds are usually used in winter and will visit a series of estates and expect keepers and others to line out around the area driven. One of the disadvantages of using the hounds is that once they have visited your estate, the keeper is usually expected to help on other estates. In this respect a visit by the hounds may mean 10 or more days absent.

- Planning the exercise is important and the Master of the hounds and keeper should work carefully to ensure Guns are placed in all suitable places; after all the hard work a fox missed is immensely annoying. Needless to say dogs – particularly reddish fox-like collies – are not allowed.

- One of the biggest problems at any fox drive by hounds is having sufficient Guns with experience at the correct location. Foxes can only be killed cleanly when close. Too great a gap between Guns can allow foxes to escape. In Finland, flag lines of plastic bags are strung on cord and hung across areas to encourage foxes to run towards Guns.

- Guns should line out quietly without talking or smoking, close to likely exit points, and face the covert with their backs against trees. They should be 40m apart.

- Heavy cartridge loads up to shot size 5 can provide a clean kill, while lighter loads may simply wound or ricochet.

- Don't forget to pull all snares before the hounds visit.

## 7.8 Bolting foxes

- One of the time honoured methods of fox control is to bolt foxes from their dens in spring using terriers. This approach has always been used in moorland areas but since it became illegal to gas foxes in dens, the method is now relied on by all moorland keepers.

- Bolting foxes requires two capable, alert men with shotguns, an obedient terrier and some purse nets. Some keepers also have a lurcher standing by for any missed fox.

- The major legal limitation of entering terriers to a fox earth is that you must ensure that badgers are not also using the earth. Entering terriers to a fox earth is legal but any use of terriers in a badger sett is illegal, even if you were unaware badgers were present.

- If you have problems with badgers and foxes co-habiting, then a licence can be applied for from the local MAFF, SOAFD or WOAD offices.

- Before entering a terrier, check the entrance carefully and quietly (no smoking). Look for the foot prints of badgers in sandy soil. and the presence of badger hairs caught on any protruding roots or stones close to the entrance. While checking the den look for all the possible exits. If you do not know the den, it is wise to have someone with you who does.

- Guns should stand down wind, concealed where necessary. With few Guns present it may be necessary to use purse nets over the exits of some holes to catch bolting foxes that could not be shot. Only enter one terrier at a time.

- There is much misunderstanding about terriers bolting foxes. A good terrier is obedient and comes out of the den when called. The idea is not for the terrier to bait the fox and return scarred and bitten but for it to locate the fox, withdraw and allow the fox to bolt within 3 minutes. Too many people favour tenacious, savage terriers which want to fight the fox and get injured themselves.

- Young cubs can sometimes be enticed from a den when the vixen is absent by gently tapping the entrance of the den and making panting sounds.

- In peaty ground check for peat runners which may allow a fox to bolt 50m away from the den. In these instances a well trained lurcher left close to an exit is as a good as a gun and with a quick shout can always catch a missed fox.

- It is essential to kill the vixen cleanly. If there are cubs present you can then lie out all night and wait for the dog fox to come back looking for the missing vixen. Even then you may not get an easy shot but it is important to kill vixen, cubs and dog.

## 7.9  Lurchers for foxes

- Over the past 15 years, more and more keepers in England and the Scottish Borders have used lurchers to assist with fox control. These provide another technique and are always a back up pair of eyes.

- Catching and killing foxes requires a lurcher with tenacity, that will hit a running fox hard and go straight for the kill. Fox lurchers do not need to be fast; but crosses are usually between a greyhound or broken-coated lurcher and a dog with some aggression such as an alsatian, doberman or bull terrier. Foxhound crosses were favoured for a while but are not used much now.

- There is a big trade in lurchers and discussions with a few knowledgeable people can often locate a dog which may be suitable for foxes. However nobody ever sells an excellent dog.

- Dogs must be broken to stock immediately; a lurcher on the loose which is not safe with stock is a serious liability.

- Lurchers have a job of work to do and it is important to remember that, for the keeper, fox control is a job and not a sport; if you can shoot a bolting fox safely, then do it; do not leave a fox for a lurcher just for the sport.

- Training a lurcher off rabbits and hares can be done but is not easy and as a rule lurchers should not be let loose in areas where any of the potential prey are present. After a while a fox-lurcher seems to know and want to kill foxes and will ignore other prey.

## 7.10  Tracing foxes

- A cover of snow on a still night in winter can leave clear and obvious marks of fox footings. Getting up early and tracing these can be a remarkably successful way of locating and killing foxes.

- Some keepers in the Scottish Highlands have had great success using snow scooters to locate and catch up with foxes in the snow.

- A dog/lurcher with a good nose can also help pick up fox footings and be an extra pair of eyes in the tracing.

- Read the signs carefully and be prepared for a fox to jump in front of you, watch the wind but also remember that a hill fox can run 30 miles in a night.

## 7.11   Fox kists and artificial earths

- A fox kist is essentially a catch-alive trap set for foxes. They are constructed from strong weldmesh and built into the side of a hill or into the entrance to a traditional den. Some are baited, some are not, but in general this is not an effective technique. Kists, like all traps, must be checked every 24 hours.

- In Scandinavia, kists are built in forestry areas out of brashings about 4m long and 1m square and then placed under branches to protect them from snow. Under each trap some grain and hay are introduced to encourage voles and attract foxes, particularly during snowy conditions.

- Kists should be dug into dry, sheltered areas and are best pre-baited with either rabbit, poultry offal or vixen urine.

- Kists with tread plates can be bought commercially or made out of large converted Larsen traps with side entrances. Commercial versions are frequently designed for urban foxes but may be too small and clean for a wily hill fox.

- Artificial earths dug on the hill can prove successful ways of catching foxes. At least you know where they are and can check on regular rounds. A fox lying in an artificial earth is not one lying in an unknown area.

- Artificial earths are usually built in dry sheltered areas from stone, with two entrances in a Y shaped pattern and a chamber at the end. The floors should be gently sloping downward from the entrances and an inspection lid can be fitted to the top.

- Artificial earths can also be constructed from concrete pipes and dug into the ground with a JCB type digger, although carrying all this kit to a remote place where a fox may lie up is not an easy task. A trigger and catching device is available to use in concrete pipe traps.

- Do not destroy fox earths in the belief that the foxes will move elsewhere. The location of a frequently used fox earth is useful to the keeper; he knows where his foxes are.

# CHAPTER EIGHT

# Control of Crow Predation

Crows are significant predators both of eggs and chicks of red grouse and active steps must be taken during spring and early summer to reduce crow predation. It seems likely that crows, in an unkeepered situation are the primary limiting factor for grouse. Good crow control is important and can usually be undertaken in the uplands quite effectively given the legal techniques available and the absence of too many nesting trees.

## 8.1 Crows and crow predation

- Crow predation is often revealed in the form of poor grouse production, detected in the July grouse count. A few good broods of six plus will be recorded and the majority of hens will be considered 'barren' where no breeding has occurred. The hens will have survived, so the ratio of hens to cocks will be similar to the ratio observed in the spring.

- Numbers of crows are increasing in the uplands, in line with the planting of forestry. Forestry provides suitable nesting habitat and a refuge for crows.

- Characteristic signs of crow predation are the sucked eggs of grouse found close to streams and under isolated trees.

- While the crow family provide a number of predators of grouse including the magpie, only the hooded crow and carrion crow are considered significant predators here. Many of the techniques for crow control apply to magpies. Rooks and jackdaws can also be killed but these are not significant grouse predators. Ravens are protected.

- Crows are highly territorial in spring and as a rule it is these birds that cause most of the damage to nesting gamebirds. Removal of these birds using Larsen traps and other techniques is the principal aim of crow control. Some of these birds may be replaced by non-territorial birds but sustained control can be highly effective.

- You should note that it is specifically forbidden by law to kill birds using snares, spring traps, poisons (all types, including narcotics and stupefying baits), bird limes, shooting at night with a lamp and shooting from a motor vehicle.

## 8.2 Larsen traps for crows: principles

- Larsen traps are designed specifically to catch territorial crows and magpies alive and unharmed using a captive bird as a lure.

- Territorial birds respond fast to intruders in their territory so when you place a trap within the bird's territory they should come quickly to try and chase the intruder from their territory. In doing so they walk around the trap and get caught.

- The trap involves a spring door to each compartment, held open by a split perch. When the inquisitive territorial bird lands on the perch, the door closes and the bird is caught. The traps are small and several can be carried in the back of a 4WD vehicle.

- Larsen trapping should start after territorial pairs are established but continue through until mid-summer since birds may be replaced.

## 8.3 Larsen traps for crows: practice

- Care of the live decoys is a requirement under the General Licence which legalises the Larsen trap. Each decoy must be provided with food, water (in an untippable container) and shelter. Food for decoys is usually provided as a split open rabbit although soaked dog foods provide a good source of food. Leftover food should be removed regularly.

- The best type of decoy is a healthy vigorous caller that actively moves about the cage: usually a recently caught bird. The presence of two perches for the decoy helps prevent stress in the captive bird and will allow the crow to hop from side to side and thus attract the attention of the territorial bird.

- Obtaining the first decoy can be a problem and some keepers will keep a couple of birds alive through the winter months. Most people try and beg or borrow a decoy from a neighbour to start them for the season. Alternatively the first decoy can be caught with an artificial nest and eggs left inside the catching enclosure. Placing the trap in a thick bush and scattering some egg shells may attract the first crow. It is illegal to trade in decoys.

- Once you have a decoy, place the trap in the open but within easy site of a perch. If this is not present crows will walk around the outside and in these instances side opening doors can be an advantage. A fencing post hammered into the ground beside the trap can help provide a perch.

- Raising the trap onto a bale of straw can increase the chances of catching but also exposes the trap to potential vandals.

- Traps must be checked daily, usually this is best done in the evening when the decoy's food and water can be topped up.

- To maximise trapping efficiency, Larsens should be moved

regularly. If the trap does not catch within two days then move it, even a few yards may be enough.

• Do not kill birds in sight of birds you still want to trap; always kill the birds humanely and discreetly. Hold the bird firmly in the left hand and give the head a sharp, very hard knock against a hard object. Game dispatch pliers are also suitable.

• Larsens can trap non-target species and just about all of these are protected by the Wildlife and Countryside Act and must be released immediately.


## 8.4  Building a Larsen trap

The following construction was designed by The Game Conservancy Trust; further information from Game Conservancy Ltd on 01425 652381. There are a number of other traps on the market, many use a wire frame and of course you may wish to design your own; further details on what is available locally can be obtained from your Game Conservancy Ltd. Advisor. As a rule we would recommend the traps are made by a joiner or bought in so the keeper can remain active on the hill.

• The trap requires the following pieces (all dimensions in mm):

WOOD:

| | | | |
|---|---|---|---|
| A | 4 pieces | 812x50x25 | Side, top and bottom rails |
| B | 4 pieces | 458x50x25 | Side pillars |
| C | 4 pieces | 762x50x25 | End, top and bottom rails |
| D | 2 pieces | 408x50x25 | End, centre pillar |
| E | 2 pieces | 762x50x25 | Division, top and bottom rail |
| F | 3 pieces | 408x50x25 | Division end and centre pillar |
| H | 2 pieces | 762x50x25 | Top and centre cross rails |
| J | 4 pieces | 330x50x25 | Trap door sides |
| K | 4 pieces | 280x50x25 | Trap door ends |

| L | 1 piece | 404x404x6 | Plywood |
| M | 1 piece | 200x165x6 | Ply access door |
| N | 2 pieces | 350x25x25 | Access door runners, rebated |
| P | 1 piece | 410x95x6 | Ply flap stop |
| Q | 1 piece | 400x400x6 | Ply division |
| | | 600x18 | Doweling for trip perches |

METAL:

| R | | 3.3m x450 | 25mm mesh netting end and sides |
| I | 1 piece | 810x810 | 25mm mesh netting, bottom |
| T | 1 piece | 400x400 | 25mm mesh netting, top |
| U | 2 pieces | 330x330 | |
| V | 1 piece | 760x450 | 25mm mesh netting, centre frame |
| | 2 pieces | 420 | 5 mm steel rod |
| | 2 pieces | | Springs for flap doors |
| | Assorted | | Nails, screws and staples |

- Construct the two side frames from parts **A** and **B** and the two centre frames with parts **E** and **F**. Note that the two outer struts **F** overlap the ends of **E** by 25 mm, and the centre rebates in **E** are to the outside of the frame. Cover with wire netting **V**.

- Make the two end frames with parts **C** and **D**.

- Lay one side frame on the floor; stand centre frame in place and fix second side to centre frame.

- Position and fix end frames. Invert and fix other side frames to centre and end frames. Fix two parts **H** into frame to give you the basic skeleton.

- Fit ply division **Q** between end frames and centre division.

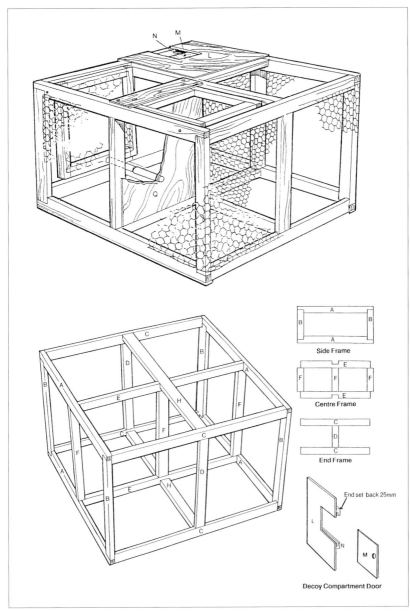

Larsen trap construction - basic assembly

97

- Construct the entrance to decoy compartment from parts **L, M** and **N**. Ensure rebated edges of parts **N** are flush with sides cut-out in part **L**. Slide door into position **M**.

- Fix completed entrance to skeleton ensuring the framework is square, the sliding door is captive on underside and the wire netting on centre frames faces into decoy compartment.

- Cover decoy compartment top, trap ends, sides and bottom with wire netting – parts **R, S** and **T**.

- Assemble trap doors from parts **J** and **K** (see diagrams) and cover with wire netting **U**.

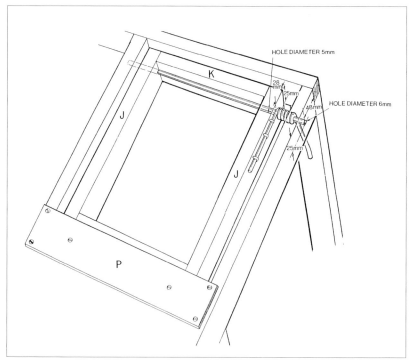

*Larsen trap construction - detail of trap door.*

- Mark and drill 6mm holes in side and centre top rails of skeleton – see diagram.

- Mark and drill 5mm holes in trap doors.

- Insert rod through 6mm hole in end frame. Position spring – use correct spring with long arm flush to trap door side. Position door aligning holes and drive rod through door into hole in centre frame. Staple long arm of spring to trap door side.

- Repeat for second trap door.

- Push doors into resting position and secure with flap stop **P**. This must be firmly attached; note the position of the six screws in the diagram of completed trap.

- Cut doweling to four pieces each 150mm long. Two for each split trip perch.

## 8.5  Cage traps for crows

- Cage traps are semi-permanent crow catching devices designed to catch both territorial and non-territorial crows and to operate through the spring and summer months.

- Traditionally cage traps have helped in the control of crows and a few well-placed traps will assist crow control greatly. Siting is all important to success.

- Traps should be sited close to regularly used flight lines, close to a loch side, shore or stream or sometimes at the junction of two valleys. Remember to choose a quiet spot away from footpaths and tracks.

- A suitable site can be tested with a Larsen trap as slight changes in location can change trapping efficiency. Smaller sectional traps are more easily moved whilst testing the suitability of sites.

- Use a decoy as with the Larsen and once again this must be provided with shelter, food and water.

## 8.6 Cage trap construction

The trap requires the following materials:

| | |
|---|---|
| 1 | 50m roll of wire netting – 1m wide |
| 1 | 20m roll of fencing wire |
| 1 | Roll of tying wire or clips |
| 5 | Poles 8cm x 2m |
| 4 | Poles 5cm x 3m |
| 4 | Poles 5cm x 1.2m |
| 4 | 8cm x 2.5cm x 2m for gate |
| Bag | 8cm Nails |
| 4 | Fencing posts |
| 1 | 20m roll of barbed wire |
| Bag | Staples |
| 1 | Coop or box for decoy |
| 1 | Water dish for decoy |

- Tools needed to construct the trap *in situ* will include: mell, claw hammer, bushman's saw, pliers, nail pullers, wire cutters.

- Trap dimensions are:
  Cage size:  2.7m x 2.7m square
  Height:     1.5m high
  Gate size:  60cm x 1.5m
  Funnel:     1m square; taper to 60cm diameter, 23cm from ground

- Erect 4 corner posts using 2m posts, and door frame.

- Tie and nail top poles (5cm x 3m) to corner posts, cutting where necessary.

- Make 1m square frame for top of funnel and hang funnel from corner posts.

- Unroll wire netting from the ground, through funnel square and thence to top rails. Ensure funnel base is 22cm from ground and 60cm in diameter and tie and staple funnel wire.

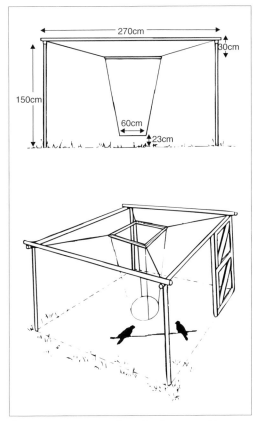

*Crow cage construction - basic assembly*

- Construct and hang door and complete netting around sides.

- Fence the trap from stock by using fencing posts and barbed wire.

*Special thanks to Sandy Massen for this construction and details.*

## 8.7 Dos and Don'ts of crow trapping

- **Do** inspect trap daily
- **Do** locate trap away from footpaths and out of sight
- **Do** keep spare decoys
- **Do** take care of decoy daily
- **Do** assist neighbours by providing decoys
- **Do** provide fresh food and water and regularly check for any escape holes
- **Do** control grass growth within and around trap
- **Do** place tunnel traps around the edge of the cage trap to catch any stoats attracted by the bait
- **Do** provide perches outside and inside the trap
- **Do** release non-target species unharmed


- **Do not** clip wing feathers of decoy. By law birds must remain free-winged
- **Do not** site cage near to cattle or sheep feed
- **Do not** site cage near a known roost
- **Do not** leave feathers or dead birds in the trap

*Above: A good selection of fire beaters appropriate for different types of moorland. Those of cheaper construction can be left on the hill for extinguishing accidental fires. (Chapter 3).*

*Below: A steel pan fire scrubber. Good on dry heathland.*

*Above: Bracken encroaches onto heather moorland, replacing heather with a plant of little value and a habitat for ticks. Correct control is essential. (Chapter 5).*

*Below: Physical control includes crushing until the bracken is exhausted.*

*Above: Medicated grit can help keep down the levels of the strongyle worm in red grouse. (Chapter 10).*

*Below: Direct dosing is a short-term but highly effective method of reducing worms in grouse just prior to breeding.*

*Above: The control of fox predation is a crucial element in the conservation of red grouse. (Chapter 7). (Photo: Laurie Campbell)*

*Below: Peregrines and other raptors are fully protected. (Chapter 15). (Photo: Laurie Campbell)*

*Above:  Large cage traps can be important in crow control. Good siting is the key. (Chapter 8).*

*Below:  Stoats are significant predators of red grouse. Approved spring traps must be set in tunnels which can be built of stones. (Chapter 9).*

*Above: A blanket drag will reveal whether ticks are present. (Chapter 11).*

*Below:  Ticks have hosts other than sheep and grouse and it may be necessary to reduce their abundance to keep louping ill under control. (Chapter 11).*

*Above: A grouse chick heavily infested with ticks so that the eye has closed. Such severe cases are rare.*

*Below: Correct practice when dipping sheep can be a key to controlling ticks and louping ill. (Chapter 11).*

*Above: Although pointers were bred for walked up shooting, they are invaluable for conducting grouse counts. (Chapter 13).*

*Below: Good keepering is the essence of red grouse conservation. Game Conservancy Ltd runs a Hill Keepers Course in alternate years, covering all aspects of management and shooting. (Chapter 14).*

# CHAPTER NINE

# Control of Stoats, Mink, Ferrets and Rabbits

While the control of fox and crow numbers is essential for good grouse production, many moor managers see the control of small ground predators as unnecessary. In some instances this may be the case and increased control of the small mustelids (stoat, mink and ferret) may have little impact on the size of the bag. Nevertheless this is not always the case and three points are relevant here.

1.  All the highly productive grouse moors in Britain carry out an intensive control programme against these predators.
2.  Detailed studies have shown that in some instances, stoats and mink can be a serious ground predator during the summer months killing incubating hens, taking eggs and killing chicks.
3.  The rates of predation by the small mustelids on gamebirds are probably a function of the abundance of alternative prey species, particularly rabbits, and the presence of suitable habitats eg. river banks for mink and walls for stoats.

## 9.1 Stoat biology

*   Stoats are larger than weasels with a relatively long tail which has a distinctive black tip. They moult twice a year and in northern Britain may turn totally white in the winter with the exception of the black tail tip: the stoat in its winter coat is known as the ermine, prized by furriers. Further south the moult is only partial or the winter coat may just be lighter.

*   Dens are frequently in walls or old piles of rocks with the remains of prey and rabbit fur made into a nest of sorts.

- Stoats are found throughout the British Isles with the exception of some of the Outer Isles (Orkney, Outer Hebrides and Arran).

- While mostly nocturnal during autumn and winter stoats become diurnal during the spring and summer, hunting along walls, banks and favoured runs.

- There is one litter of 6-12 young produced each April; males play no part in rearing the brood. Females may move the family and it is not uncommon to see whole families dispersing in July.

- The abundance of stoats is determined by the abundance of their main food source, which in Britain is rabbits. Stoats appear unable to control rabbit numbers.

- Keepers on hill ground usually kill between one and eight stoats per 1km$^2$ of heather moorland per annum (4-16 per 1000 acres) but this varies according to keepers efforts and the abundance of rabbits. Before myxomatosis Scottish keepers were killing on average up to 80 stoats a year but more recently the average Scottish keeper is killing 20 per annum.

- Stoats are legally protected in Eire but not in the United Kingdom.


## 9.2 Weasel biology

- Weasels are about half to two thirds the size of a stoat and have no black tip to their tail.

- Coat and behaviour is much like the stoat with some individuals becoming totally white during the winter months.

- Weasels are present throughout Great Britain but absent in Ireland and some of the Outer Isles, including the Isle of Man, Islay, Jura, Arran, Mull, Outer Hebrides, Orkney and Shetland.

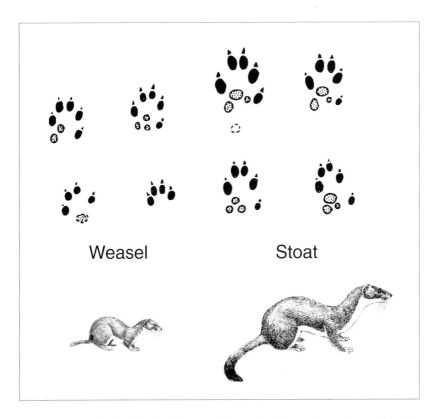

Weasel    Stoat

- Weasels feed principally on voles and other rodents but will take eggs and small birds, including young gamebirds. Occasionally they will take large prey species up to the size of a hare but this is thought uncommon and we know of no known record of a weasel actually killing an adult grouse.

- Weasels produces one or two litters with an average of six young per litter.

- Abundance of weasels is highly variable depending on the abundance of voles but keepers usually catch twice as many stoats as weasels in their tunnel traps. In recent years some Scottish estates have been trapping up to eight weasels per km$^2$.

105

### 9.3 Polecat and Ferret Biology

- True polecats were previously distributed throughout Britain but numbers are now restricted to Wales and the Western Midlands as a consequence of persecution by keepers. Numbers are increasing however and spreading. Most 'polecats' killed by keepers are in fact escaped ferrets.

- Polecats can be killed legally but under Schedule 6 of The Wildlife & Countryside Act (1981) spring traps and certain other methods cannot be used.

- In general polecats are not common on high hill ground but are found in marginal ground or forestry plantations. However, ferrets are more likely to move onto the hill and in some places, like Mull, are regularly found on open moorland.


### 9.4 Mink biology

- Mink are not native to Britain but became established after escaping or being released from fur farms. Self sustaining populations were present in parts of Britain by the end of the 1950s.

- Mink are relatively large compared to stoats, usually with a dark chocolate brown coat and white chin patch.

- Mink are generally found close to water courses but may move away from rivers where alternative prey, particularly rabbits are abundant.

- Mink take a wide range of food species and simply take what is available, usually ducks, rabbits or other similar sized prey items, including grouse.

Mink

## 9.5 Signs of predation by small mustelids

- The characteristic sign of stoat and weasel predation is a dead bird or rabbit killed by a bite to the neck. Incubating birds are particularly vulnerable. Freshly killed birds may not be eaten but a careful inspection and plucking of feathers around the neck of a bird 'found dead' will reveal the characteristic bite, bruising and some bleeding under the skin.

- Small mustelids frequently devour the birds from the neck and burrow into the chest muscles leaving most of the body untouched but a large hole where they have fed.

- Small mustelids will remove eggs from the nests of gamebirds, roll them away and then leave them 'sucked' in a den. Some keepers have reported finding in excess of 100 grouse eggs accumulated in old walls where stoats have taken them.

- Chicks and young birds will be taken, sometimes carried back to the den for the young or sometimes partially buried in holes or under rocks.

- Droppings of all mustelids are generally like ferret droppings, long thin and black, with remains of food, mostly fur and feathers, and a characteristic twist of fur at each end.

## 9.6  Planning the control of small mustelids.

- The control of these small mustelids should take the form of a two-pronged approach. First, the direct control of the mustelids themselves, particularly in spring when the animals are highly active prior to the gamebird breeding season when they exert their greatest impact. Second, the indirect control of the mustelids by the control of their principle food sources, usually rabbits.

- The priority for direct control within an upland estate should be to eradicate mink and ferrets and to control stoats intensely during spring and early summer. Weasels are generally not thought to be significant on upland estates but the occasional one may be caught.

- Mink traps can run through much of the year and once a standard trapping line is set along a river course this should help to keep the area clear. However since the traps must by law be checked every 24 hours most keepers run their traps only through spring and summer, thereafter leaving them *in situ* but closed.

- For stoat control, the basic strategy should be for each keeper to run more than 100 spring traps in tunnels from late winter through to August. These should be strategically placed around the hill ground in walls, hedges or banks, with traps on the hill along hill roads, walls, stream sides, sheep rubs and under piles of stones.

- Remember that traps must be checked every 24 hours, so design the trap line for an easy walk which enables other jobs to be done and allows you to check your game and for signs of other predators *en route*.

- Rabbit control is an integral part of predator control. Many of the predators are dependent on the rabbit resource and reducing the abundance of rabbits should reduce the abundance and immigration rate of predators such as the small mustelids and foxes.

- Prior to myxomatosis, more keepers were employed and rabbit control was an important task for the keeper, the estate rabbit catcher and the shepherd. Now there are less people employed for the task and with fewer techniques available there has been a reduction in the number killed.

- Rabbit control is best undertaken when rabbits are severely challenged by weather conditions. When snow and weather conditions are poor in winter, rabbits should be reduced and even eliminated from local areas.

## 9.7 Controlling stoats in tunnel traps

- Tunnel traps are spring traps placed in natural or artificial tunnels suitable for the catching of small mustelids and rats. The usual spring trap is the Fenn trap; the gin trap is illegal.

- Note that the Fenn trap and other similar spring traps must be set in a tunnel. It is illegal to set these traps without suitable covering since they may inadvertently catch protected species or livestock by the leg.

- Tunnels can be made *in situ* with pieces of stone and wood, using natural holes in trees or banks or cutting a trench and covering the top with a turf. The most efficient method of constructing a legal and effective tunnel trap is to make it out of wood and then place it in the desired location, building it into the local habitat with stones and heather turves.

- Many keepers use 'slab wood' or bark-off cuts, although bricks, turves and pipes of various sorts can be used. The tunnels should be 45cm long and just high enough to allow the Fenn trap to close when sprung freely. For the Fenn Mark IV this is a height of 13cm with a 15cm wide base.

- Traps should be weathered before use, as described for the weathering of fox snares (7.4). Traps can be buried or left outside to lose the smell of factories, grease and humans. Some keepers wax their traps to prevent rusting and to allow them to spring easily. While it is not necessary to wear gloves when setting traps, rub your hands with soil to remove characteristic human smells.

- Traps are sometimes set without bait, although many keepers like to smear rabbit liver under the plate of the trap. If a female stoat or other mustelid is caught in season then drops of her urine should be squeezed onto the plate of the trap and this will be highly attractive to the more wide ranging males and is without doubt the most attractive bait available for a male stoat.

- Before setting the trap, check its sensitivity so that it goes off with a slight pressure on the pad. In some instances the plate may have to be bent or the trigger filed smooth.

- Set traps should be placed well back into the middle of the tunnel so that inquisitive game, dogs or birds of prey will not be accidentally caught. Traps should be secured using the chain, either by stapling to the tunnel, or with a peg. If the set trap is placed in a small, saucer shaped hollow leaving the trap plate flush with the ground this will be more likely to catch the crafty stoat.

- Practice setting traps and have them checked by an experienced trapper before setting for real. There are stories of inexperienced keepers becoming incapacitated with their thumbs caught inadvertently in a Fenn trap.

- Place sticks across the tunnel entrance to leave a gap small enough for a stoat to squeeze in but prevent a bird entering. In areas where pine martens are present care should be taken to ensure sticks are 6cm apart. Pine martens are a protected species.

- Traps should be regularly reset whether they have caught or not.

- Mustelids are curious and will seek out and investigate the tunnels but small paths will help to guide the passing stoat. The art is to think like a mustelid and know a good place. Careful pruning to keep paths open during the summer is a good idea.

- Traps should be placed so a keeper can walk his trap line, checking traps as he goes, alert for other predators and keeping an eye on his grouse. The trap line should be placed to provide a walk of the ground that the keeper should cover each day. A good and easy trap line can be constructed along a hill road with traps dug into the side of the hill road so the keeper can drive slowly around and over the hill each day and check the traps. Checking lines from a vehicle must not be considered a total substitute for other trap lines that require checking on foot.

- Fenn traps are available from:

  A Fenn & Co, Hoopers Lane, Astwood Bank, Redditch, Worcestershire B96 6AR
  or   Game Conservancy Ltd
  or   Some agricultural suppliers and shooting/tackle shops.


## 9.8  Dogs and squeaking

- Stoats and other small mustelids are inquisitive and can be attracted by making rabbit squeaking noises (7.6). Once within shot the animal can be dispatched.

- Some dogs are also very efficient at locating and killing stoats. We have found the German Pointers we use for our research have a predilection for stoats and regularly point, catch and kill stoats.

- Terriers can also be used to locate a stoat den and to work banks and walls where stoats may be active.


## 9.9  Mink traps

- Mink are essentially a riverine species and while they will move out onto the hill, an effective trapping system along water courses will reduce the abundance of these voracious predators.

- Fortunately mink are not trap shy and they can be caught in tunnel traps or in special cage traps designed for catching mink. These traps are both strong and effective and can be purchased through trap dealers and suppliers of game management equipment.

- Mink traps should be placed close to river crossings, such as under a small footbridge or under a bank where a mink is likely to run.

- Traps should be placed at 70m intervals along the stream. Once a good location is found the traps should continue to catch mink moving into the area.

- Baiting traps is not necessary, although fish guts can help attract a passing mink's attention.

- Mink in traps are highly aggressive and are best dispatched within the trap with a low velocity air pistol.

## 9.10  Controlling rabbits

- Stoat numbers are strongly linked to the abundance of their main food source, rabbits. During the myxomatosis outbreak when rabbit numbers were low during the 1950s and 1960s, numbers of stoats killed by keepers fell dramatically, in line with the fall in rabbit numbers.

- Effective stoat control should include the control of rabbits. Rabbit control can be undertaken throughout the year but is most effective before the breeding season when the rabbit population is stressed from harsh weather conditions. Remember to hit the rabbits hard when numbers are down. They are so productive that trying to control them during the summer months will have little impact on population size.

- There is a wide range of techniques for controlling rabbits; a few of the more popular ones used on upland estates are noted here:

- Dazzling rabbits at night with a lamp and then using a .22 rifle to kill the rabbits, although these actions may disturb foxes. Lurchers can be used but invariably disturb other rabbits.

- Ferreting holes. When snow is down it is clear which holes are being used by rabbits and bolting rabbits with ferrets either into nets or to be killed by a shotgun can prove a good method of control.

- Flip top box traps have become popular on some upland estates within the past few years. These traps must be used in combination with rabbit netting to ensure rabbits run over the traps. Ideal sites are alongside forestry plantations. These traps are set into the ground on rabbit runs and left so rabbits can run across the top for a period of time. Then one evening the traps are set so that each rabbit that runs across the top is 'flipped' into the $60cm^3$ cellar. Traps are then emptied the following morning. The traps can be bought from a number of manufacturers such as Brechin Castle Saw Mill, Balmanno Estate, Lauderdale Engineering Ltd., Lee & Carnwarth Estates. Contact your local Game Conservancy Ltd Advisor for your nearest supplier.

CHAPTER TEN

# Control of the Strongyle Worm

The parasitic nematode known to scientists as *Trichostrongylus tenuis* and to keepers and moor managers as the strongyle worm can cause regular and large scale reductions in the abundance of grouse on 'cyclic' grouse moors and occasionally similar effects on 'non-cyclic' moors. In most of northern England and parts of Scotland control strategies against the nematode are essential to ensure long term bag returns. Indeed in some years efforts against the nematode on well managed estates can be as important as predator control. Nevertheless actively controlling worms should only be undertaken when the parasites are a significant or rising problem and not as an alternative to the traditional techniques of good habitat management and legal predator control.

## 10.1 Life cycle of the strongyle worm

- The parasitic worm that causes the disease strongylosis lives in the twin blind-ended tubes  situated at the end of the birds main gut and known as the caeca. Grouse have exceptionally large caeca (75cm) to cope with their poor fibrous diet. When removing the guts of grouse you may notice parts of the gut have distinctive light stripes running down their length: these are the caeca.

- The worms mate within the birds caeca; the females produce large quantities of eggs which pass from the grouse in the 'caecal droppings'. These are not the hard fibrous kind with the white tip at the end, but the brown viscous 'chocolate mousse' droppings left close to the roosting pile each morning. Frequently two piles of caecal droppings are left, one from each caecum.

- The eggs develop within the caecal droppings, producing free-living stages that feed on bacteria and other suitable material within the droppings. The final stage, the infective larvae, do not feed but leave the droppings and, using the water film around the heather plant, make their way to the growing tip of the heather, where a feeding grouse may then ingest the larvae.

- Development of the parasites requires damp conditions and a temperature greater than 6°C. When the temperature is colder, the parasites do not develop but may remain alive. When warmer, the larvae develop faster and become more active but use up their reserves faster and do not live so long.

- Once the parasites have been ingested and matured they do not multiply within the grouse themselves but produce eggs that pass out in the dropping and subsequently infect the same or other grouse.

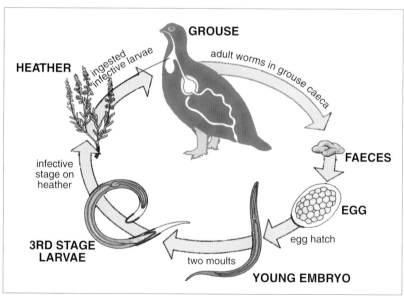

*Life cycle of the strongyle worm*

- When the infective larvae enter the grouse they make their way to the caeca and develop into adult worms, that burrow into the caecal wall of the grouse. However in winter some of these infective larvae do not develop immediately into adults but remain in an inert stage known as arrested development. They continue development in the following spring.

- Grouse become infected with the nematode worm during two periods. The first is during late summer when all worms entering the grouse develop into adults. The later and larger increase in parasites is in early spring, when the arrested larvae picked up during the winter months continue their development into adults and, more important, the undeveloped larvae on the vegetation develop into infective larvae.

## 10.2 Effects of the strongyle worm on red grouse

- The strongyle worm burrows into the caecal wall causing internal bleeding and reducing the digestive efficiency and condition of the grouse.

- The largest effects of the parasite are during early spring when food quality is at its worst. The arrested and infective larvae are developing into adults and the grouse are stressed by the activities of breeding, including the cock's defence of territories and the hen's need to obtain sufficient nutrients to produce a clutch of eggs and to sustain her through the 22 days of incubation.

- Weak and dead grouse are frequently observed from late February onwards. The classic sign of a weak bird is the poor 'owl like' flight. When disturbed, birds glide, usually down-hill, showing no strong wing beats. Some weak birds are found sitting in the heather with little muscle on the chest but often a large bolus of food in the crop.

- Dead birds can be found throughout the hill but usually end up low down in gutters or stream sides and appear severely emaciated. Removal of guts will show enlarged caeca with blood spots.

- Heavily infected birds will produce diarrhoea like caecal droppings – more runny and smelly than the normal droppings and often lighter in colour than the normal chocolate brown viscous droppings.

- Grouse with more than 3000 worms per bird generally exhibit reduced condition.

- Worm burdens increase dramatically in wet conditions when grouse density is high.

- On wet blanket bog moorland, the over-riding factor determining infection rate is the density of birds, since the habitat is usually wet and suitable for larval development.

- On dry freely-drained hills, high grouse density need not lead to outbreaks of infection because a large proportion of the larvae die, but following a wet summer rates of infection can increase and lead to an outbreak.

## 10.3 Worm counts

- Regular assessment of worm burdens in your grouse population is a sensible monitoring precaution.

- Worm counts from old grouse shot during the autumn reflect what the worm burdens were during the previous breeding season and may bear no relation to levels in the following breeding season. The gain of worms in early spring is a major factor determining the condition and breeding production of grouse.

- Ideally worm counts should be conducted from pre-breeding birds in spring but this is not possible except under licence, unless dead grouse can be collected from road kills or fence strikes. It is not unusual for a few birds to die each spring with high worm burdens; having these analysed does not necessarily mean that an outbreak is imminent. A random sample of birds is really required, usually 10 old and 10 young.

- Counting eggs of worms from the caecal droppings is not accurate since there is a great deal of variation in egg production. Low counts tell you nothing but high counts do indicate that some birds are heavily infected.

- Worm counts can be conducted by a number of organisations including Game Conservancy Ltd Advisors and the Scottish Agricultural Colleges, although both have to make a charge.

## 10.4 Conducting worm counts

- Should you wish to undertake your own worm counts then this is possible with a sink, water source and suitable equipment. However it is a good idea to have your methods checked by an expert. Select a grouse; conduct a worm count on one of the caeca and give the expert the other. The two counts should be within 10% of each other.

- Equipment needed:
  2 – specialised sieves: 1 with 810µm mesh and 1 with
        212µm mesh
  1 – pair of dissecting scissors
  1 – 300 or 500ml measuring cylinder
  1 – petri dish
  1 – anglepoise lamp
  1 – high sided washing tray (photographic type)
  1 – 15ml syringe (no needle)
  1 – 500ml glass beaker

This equipment is available from scientific equipment suppliers such as Fisons Scientific Equipment (01509 616101) although it may be easier to buy through a scientific laboratory or organisation.

- Before starting the count make a note of the bird's age, sex, date of death and probable cause of death.

- Place the two sieves in the sink with the larger mesh sieve (810µm) on top. The sink should be set up with a continual but medium flow of water and an over-flow pipe that allows the water level to stay slightly lower than the top sieve. One way of getting the level right is to insert a pipe of the right diameter into the plug hole and cut to a length just less than the height of the two sieves.

- Remove the gut from the dead grouse by making a small incision above the cloaca (anus), inserting your first and second finger up the rib cage and around the birds gizzard and then gently pulling the gut out. Snip the end of the gut from the body. The guts can be stored in a freezer in individual plastic bags but the bags should be marked with a reference number or at least the bird's age and date of death.

- Tease the guts apart and identify the two blind ending caeca; they are long with feint stripes along their length and grow from the end of the hind gut. Note they are held in position by tissue which will break easily as you tease them out but take care not to break the caeca. Remove one caecum by snipping it from the end of  the gut, cut along its length and then cut into three or four roughly equal parts.

- Place the caecal pieces in the top sieve with the water flow playing on them gently. The water should keep the caecal parts washing round and round carefully so any worms are gently washed from the gut, pass through the sieve and are caught in the finer sieve underneath.

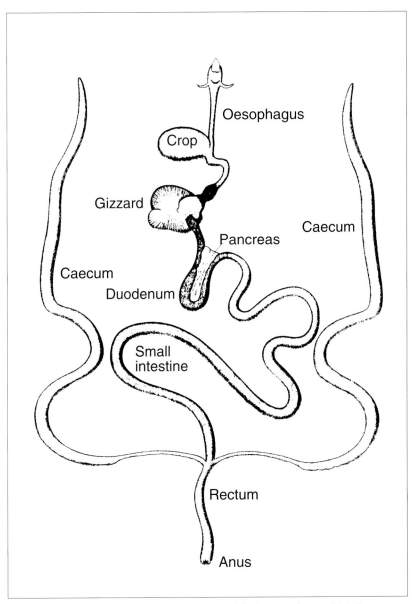

*The dissected grouse gut, showing the two blind caeca from which the worms are counted.*

- Let the caecal parts wash for about 10 minutes or until the caecal wall becomes clear.

- Discard the contents of the upper sieve. Remove the lower sieve and place upside down on the high sided washing tray, then wash out the contents of the sieve with 300ml of water (measured in the cylinder) and collect in the wash tray.

- Pour the water and sieve contents into a 500ml beaker and stir gently to ensure worms are evenly distributed throughout the beaker. Remove 10ml of the water from the beaker with the 15ml syringe and empty into the petri dish.

- Place the petri dish on a dark background (e.g. black tile) with the anglepoise light positioned low so that the light clearly shows each of the worms. Identify some of the worms and note their size, shape and general characteristics in comparison to any pieces of mucous that may have been washed through. Some of the worms will be broken, so count all full worms and worms that are more than half the length of the average worm. Note that lines scratched on the base of the petri dish will allow you to keep your place while counting the worms.

- Take a total of 3 samples from the beaker, ensuring that each sample is only taken after the water has been gently stirred to ensure that worms have not sunk to the bottom of the beaker.

- The number of worms per bird is calculated by adding the 3 counts together, multiplying by 10 to estimate the number per 300ml and then multiplying this by 2 to obtain the number per bird (see table 10.4.1).

- To estimate the average number of worms per bird needs a slight modification from the normal calculation. This is because worm burdens are aggregated within the grouse population, with a few grouse carrying high worm burdens and a large proportion

| | Calculator actions | Figures |
|---|---|---|
| Count 1 (10 mls) | | 42 |
| Count 2 (10 mls) | | 39 |
| Count 3 (10 mls) | | 41 |
| Worms in 30 mls | (add Counts 1+2+3) | 122 |
| Worms in 300 mls | (Multiply by 10) | 1220 |
| Worms in this bird | (Multiply by 2) | 2440 |

Table 10.4.1. A worked example for estimating the number of worms per bird following 3 counts.

| | Actual Worm Count | Logarithm of Worm Count | Action on Calculator |
|---|---|---|---|
| Bird 1 | 1060 | 3.025 | 1060 "Log" |
| Bird 2 | 2030 | 3.307 | 2030 "Log" |
| Bird 3 | 3750 | 3.574 | 3750 "Log" |
| Bird 4 | 960 | 2.982 | 960 "Log" |
| Bird 5 | 8080 | 3.907 | 8080 "Log" |
| Number of birds | 5 | 5 | 5 |
| Arithmetic mean | 3176 | 3.359 | (Bird 1+2+3+4+5)/5 |
| Geometric mean | | 2287 | Anti-log($10^x$) |

Table 10.4.2. A worked example for calculating geometric average worm burdens – the corrected average. Here we take the average of 5 different worm counts. Note that the true average calculated with Logarithms is less than the average calculated using the normal arithmetic procedure. The geometric calculation reduces the biases introduced by one large count.

carrying low worm burdens. Expressing worm counts as the normal arithmetic average (sum all and divide by number) provides a biased estimate larger than the true average.

- Average worm counts are best expressed as the geometric means. Geometric means are calculated by converting each worm count

123

into Logarithms (using a calculator) adding these together and then dividing by the number of samples. Taking the Anti-logarithm of this figure (sometimes shown as $10^x$) gives the geometric average (see table 10.4.2 for worked example).

## 10.5 Reducing worms by direct dosing

- Direct dosing is a short-term but highly effective method for reducing worms in heavily infected grouse just prior to breeding.

- The principle is to catch grouse and dose each individual with an anthelmintic and so kill the worms and allow the grouse to return to good condition before the breeding season.

- Remember that the major reason for dosing is to improve breeding condition of hens so breeding production and bag size are increased. If a grouse is so heavily infected it was going to die then dosing may be too late to save that individual although there have been instances where this has worked.

- Treatment can take place any time between the end of the shooting season and the beginning of the breeding season. Generally dosing should be undertaken during suitable conditions up to 15 April, although you may have to cease earlier in South Yorkshire and you may continue into May in parts of northern Scotland.

- Timing is important; the more birds treated after the spring rise of worms the better. Nevertheless dosing in autumn is not necessarily a waste of time; killing worms benefits the grouse. Birds treated at this time of the year still have improved breeding production.

- Some keepers dose twice, catching and treating in autumn after the shooting season has been completed and then recatching and treating birds in early spring.

- The technique is to dazzle grouse at night with a strong light, catch them in a net and then treat them with Nilverm.

## 10.6 Direct dosing in practice

- Ideal lamping nights for grouse are like good nights for lamping rabbits. They should be windy but not too windy, dark with no moon and with no rain or snow. One rough rule is that if you can see your shadow or the silhouette of the hill clearly you will probably be better off staying at home.

- Before setting off to catch grouse make sure you have a lamp, net, and the dosing equipment in your pocket.

- It is advisable and easier to work in pairs, both of you can catch and walk on parallel beats across the hill but take care not to point the lights at each other when catching.

- The basic technique is to walk across the hill, scanning the ground in front and looking specifically for the eye reflections of the grouse. Remember that the sound or the sight of you will make the bird take flight.

- Walk straight towards the bird you have seen; it is usually the cock so look around for the hen. She is usually within 5m of the cock but may have her head lower. You want to selectively dose the hens, so walk around the cock and up to the hen. When you are close, within a step and a half, swing the net around and over the hen.

- If all has gone to plan you should have your hen in the net. Keep the net firmly on the ground, hold the hen securely but not tightly and remove her from the net. Take care not to grab her by the tail, and keep her wings closed. If the cock is still present swing your light straight onto him, pass the hen to your colleague and catch the cock as well.

- Take care when you are holding birds. Do not squeeze the bird or hold it tight or keep it in a place where it may become hot. On the other hand, you do not want to hold the bird so loosely that it flaps its wings.

- Before you start treating the birds, lay out your equipment for dosing and tagging so all is available and easy to reach. Fill the syringe with sufficient Nilverm to treat a grouse; this will depend on the concentration and there should be a guide on the side of the container. A hen grouse will weigh 650 to 700gm and a cock up to 850gm.

- The bird is best held firmly under the left arm and with the head and neck straight. Open the mouth by pulling down gently on the lower bill, insert the tubing over the tongue and gently down the throat. Take care not to damage the bird; the tube can go no further than the crop. Slowly push the plunger on the syringe and remove the tube.

- As a rule it is good practice to tag the bird with a numbered Quadtag and to note when and where the bird was treated. Small reflective coloured strips can be inserted onto the tag so that treated birds can be seen again at night and not recaught. These tags should be about 4cm long and 2cm wide so the grouse can preen them into their feathers.

- Release the birds immediately. Do not throw the birds in the air but place them carefully under some thick heather and even pull some heather up to place over their heads. They will sit quiet while you withdraw to look for the next bird to catch.

- With a good density of grouse you should catch up to 50 grouse a night.

- For further details on catching equipment and the technique for direct dosing, contact the Advisors of Game Conservancy Ltd.

## 10.7  Reducing worms by medicated grit

- An indirect method of reducing worm burdens in grouse is to apply grit treated with an anthelmintic drug which will kill worms, reduce the egg production of surviving worms and reduce the development of larvae.

- Grouse store grit within their gizzards, where they use it to grind up the tough and fibrous heather plants. Grit is often referred to as the 'teeth of the grouse'.

- Medicated grit should not be considered an alternative method to direct dosing but an additional technique used to keep levels of worm infection low. Nevertheless it is neither economical nor wise to apply medicated grit in places where worms are not, and will not be, a problem to the grouse population.

- Medicated grit is ordinary grit coated with a fat that incorporates the active ingredient Fenbendazole, sold by Hoechst Animal Health under the commercial name of Panacur. This drug is not

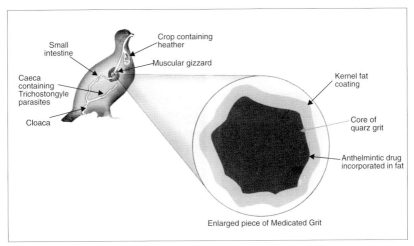

*The structure and use of medicated grit.*

127

soluble in water, does not break down in sunlight and is safe to wildlife and stock at rates exceeding 1000 times the recommended dose.

- The Panacur drug is used because it is both environmentally safe and because its efficacy is greater when administered as a series of small split doses, precisely the way in which grouse eat grit.

- Medicated grit is sold by
  Strathclyde Chemical Co. Ltd, High Street, Johnstone, Renfrewshire PA5 8SP
  (01505 31611).


## 10.8  Medicated grit in practice

- Establish a gritting system on the moor with ordinary Cornish quartz grit or similar quality grit which is neither too soft nor too large nor too flaky. A ton of grit should cover $10km^2$ or 2500 acres; more if a gritting system is already established.

- Grit piles should be placed out in a lattice pattern with about 250m between piles, giving several piles in each grouse territory.

- Each pile of grit should be between 0.5kg and 1kg (1-2 lb.), scooped out from a bag with a plastic bottle or some other similar device. Grit should be placed on a raised and preferably hard substrate such as a protruding rock. Do not place grit too high and if there is no obvious place, then cut and turn over a divot of heather for the grouse grit to sit on.

- Grit piles should be put in obvious places for the grouse and generally on the edge of burnt heather or a slight rise. In harsh snowy conditions grouse can become short of grit, so grit placed on hill areas which will blow clear could be beneficial during winter.

- Some keepers have used a wide range of artificial holders for grit including old tomato boxes and cut down car tyres.

- Grit piles should be established during the late summer before broods start breaking up and young grouse start establishing territories. Do not be too concerned about natural grit; grouse will take artificial grit even when there are suitable supplies of natural grit.

- Medicated grit should be added to the piles of natural grit after the shooting season has finished. Walk the hill in late October if shooting has finished and place medicated grit on the piles of grit that have clearly been used by grouse. For the first season, work on about a ton to every 40km$^2$ or 10000 acres. This is not a hard and fast figure and depends on the hill and the density of grouse.

- Grit should not be placed on the hill after 15 April. This is to allow the warm weather during the summer to denature the active ingredient and ensure that grouse are not carrying the active drug within 24 days of 12 August, the legal 'withdrawal period'.

# CHAPTER ELEVEN

# Control of Ticks and Louping Ill

Ticks are blood sucking, spider-like creatures that can be seen buried into the skin of their hosts feeding on the host's blood. They frequently bite in places that the host has difficulty reaching to preen or groom and can be seen around the eyes and ears of many animals. Ticks themselves are little more than a nuisance to most of their hosts but the diseases they transmit can cause serious mortality, particularly to grouse.

## 11.1  Biology of ticks

*   The tick life cycle consists of four major stages: egg, larvae, nymph and adult. The larvae, nymph and adult female take blood meals and must do so to develop and survive to the next stage or, in the case of the adult female, to produce eggs.

*   Adult female ticks produce large egg masses that hatch into larvae in the following spring. These larvae then climb the vegetation and seek (quest) a host to obtain a blood meal before falling from the host and developing into a nymph. The nymphs quest again and have a second blood meal before developing into adults. The adult female feeds but the males do not; they seek and mate with the female on the host.

*   The larvae are small, have only 6 legs and are the most abundant stage. Larvae that have successfully fed fall from the host onto the vegetation and then burrow into the base of the vegetation where they develop into the next stage. The damper and thicker the basal mat layer the better the ticks survive. Vegetation with a thick basal mat such as purple moor-grass (*Molinia*), rushes and bracken can support relatively high tick populations.

- Tick activity can occur during one of two periods. Ticks are active in most months of the year but become numerous (the 'tick rise') principally in May and June, with an occasional second rise around September. Many of the ticks fail to find a host and subsequently die, principally from drying out.

- Nymphs are larger than larvae and have 8 legs but unlike males do not have their back totally covered by a shield. After a meal they also fall into the mat vegetation and develop into the adult stage. Adult females invariably feed on a mammalian host like a sheep, hare or a deer.

- The life cycle from egg through to production of a second egg batch may take as little as two years but may be extended to four or more years depending on the availability of suitable hosts and damp areas to survive the winter months.

- While the ticks are sucking blood they may ingest a range of parasites from the host, including the virus that causes the disease louping ill. When an infected tick subsequently bites another host it can infect the new host and thus transmit the disease from one host to the next.

## 11.2 Biology of louping ill

- The virus passes from the ticks to the host in the saliva of the ticks. Once inside the host the virus multiplies and infects the hosts central nervous system, causing serious problems with locomotion which can ultimately lead to death.

- Infected sheep 'loup', that is to say they are unable to walk properly and fall over. However, joint-ill, a blood infection with a bacterium, and other diseases may cause similar symptoms. Joint-ill is present in all sheep flocks that are bitten by ticks but louping ill is not present in all tick populations.

- Once a sheep has become infected with the virus, the concentration of virus in the blood rises rapidly. During the period of this viraemia, ticks feeding on the sheep blood can become infected with the virus. However, the sheep produces antibodies to kill the virus, reducing the concentration of virus in the blood, after which the sheep will probably not pass it on.

- Between 10% and 60% of infected sheep die from louping ill, depending on the breed of the sheep, nutrition and past exposure to the disease.

- Like sheep, grouse also show a strong viraemia and ticks feeding on the grouse become infected. Grouse mortality is high, with 80% of infected grouse dying. Characteristic signs are often seen in grouse 4 to 6 weeks of age, with some incapable of walking and flying.

- Other hosts on the hill become infected with the virus when bitten by an infectious tick but then develop an immune response. No viraemia or symptoms develop. Only the grouse and the sheep consistently produce a viraemic response of sufficient concentration for feeding ticks to become infected.

- The non-viraemic hosts such as deer and hares may be considered dead ends for the virus but since they develop immunity and produce antibodies, testing their blood for antibody will demonstrate if the disease is present within them.

## 11.3 Assessing the moor for ticks

- Ticks and tick borne diseases like louping ill will not be a problem when ticks are absent, so the first step is to identify if ticks are present.

- Ticks require a mammalian host (sheep, deer or hare) to complete their life cycle so the first place to start is to ask the shepherd and conduct a tick search of his flock. Examine sheep before dipping and the carcasses of deer and mountain hares shot during the summer or autumn. Rabbits do not carry many ticks so do not bother to look at them.

- An alternative approach is to use a surrogate host such as yourself and to walk with thick woolly socks through areas of coarse grass or bracken in May or June.

- Grouse chicks caught within the first 2-3 weeks of June may have ticks around their eyes. Great care should be taken when locating and catching grouse chicks, as they can easily be stood on. Ideally a highly trained pointer with an experienced field worker should be used.

- Ticks will also attach to an old sheep skin or blanket dragged across the vegetation, particularly in May and June, although nothing seems to attract ticks better than a hill shepherd who has been handling his flock.

- To make a blanket drag requires: an old white woollen blanket, 2 broom handles or old light conduit cut to the width of the blanket, a ball of baler twine, a drill and a knife.

- Cut 4 small holes at regular intervals along the leading edge of the blanket and thread 4 pieces of 10cm twine through each. Lie the first broomstick along the leading edge of the blanket, drill 4 holes in the broom handle and tie the broomstick to the blanket.

- Tie 3 x 1m lengths of baler twine to the broomstick, one at one end, one a third of the way along the broomstick and the third two-thirds along the broomstick. Tie the other broomstick to the other end.

133

- The blanket drag should be constructed so that it is comfortable enough for you to walk along holding the free broomstick with the blanket lying flat on the ground and rubbing the top of the vegetation without being disturbed by your footsteps.

- To determine if ticks are present choose some 'ticky' vegetation which has a good thick matt layer underneath such as old bracken beds or rushy grass.

- During the summer, walk for about 50m with the blanket flowing carefully over the vegetation so that any questing ticks will be picked up; ensure the blanket does not float. Choose a morning with little wind and no direct sun. At the end of the drag gently turn the blanket over and inspect the underside for ticks. Take care – the small larvae are difficult to see to begin with but quite easy once you get your eye in. A white blanket is necessary to see them.

- Blanket drags do not necessarily give a good picture of tick abundance because they only sample the ticks that have yet to reach a host. For example, in an area where the ticks have already reached a host your blanket drag may show no ticks present while in fact such an area is of great importance to the tick population.

- The larval stages of the ticks are not spread evenly across the vegetation but concentrated in certain hot spots because they have just emerged from a females egg mass. A large number of larvae may not mean lots of ticks over a wide area.

## 11.4  Assessing the grouse for louping ill

- If you are not sure if louping ill is present in a grouse population your first visit should be to the local shepherds to ask if they vaccinate against the disease. However, be aware that other diseases, including some tick borne diseases, may cause similar symptoms. Louping ill is difficult to diagnose on clinical signs alone.

- If your neighbour's grouse moor has louping ill, there is a reasonable probability that the disease is also in your grouse population but only if ticks are present. However, note that many landowners do not like to admit they have the disease in their grouse since this will tend to reduce the capital value of the moor, even if they are shooting reasonable numbers of grouse.

- A visit to the veterinary surgeon or a discussion with your local Veterinary Investigation Centre or Scottish Agricultural College may reveal whether samples have been collected from your hill and tested. However, vets are careful not to break the confidence of their clients and may only indicate in approximate terms if louping ill has been recorded in the general vicinity.

- The only true way to identify the presence of louping ill is to remove the brains of an infected grouse and use sophisticated laboratory techniques to identify the virus. The simpler method is to look for antibody to the virus from blood samples of animals that could have been exposed to the disease.

- The antibodies to the virus lie in the clear portion of blood known as the serum. Blood samples should be collected by a qualified veterinary surgeon from sheep or other hosts and then left to stand overnight to allow the clotted blood to separate. In the morning decant the clear sera into a second bottle, taking care not to contaminate it with the blood clot. Label carefully and store in the freezer.

- Serum samples can then be analysed through your local vet, VI centre or SAC although all will have to send the samples away to a specialised laboratory. Testing samples can be expensive, so check on the price before you start and carefully select the most suitable host. This is usually an adult ewe that has not been vaccinated and even better an adult ewe that has not been dipped against ticks. Other hosts can then be sampled if desired.

135

- With 80% mortality amongst infected grouse, any grouse samples that prove positive reflect a large proportion that have died (see Table 11.4).

| Percentage of grouse LI positive | Percentage exposed to LI | Percentage dead from LI |
|---|---|---|
| 2% | 9% | 4% |
| 5% | 21% | 17% |
| 10% | 36% | 29% |
| 15% | 47% | 38% |
| 20% | 56% | 44% |
| 25% | 63% | 50% |
| 30% | 68% | 55% |
| 40% | 77% | 62% |
| 50% | 83% | 67% |
| 60% | 88% | 71% |
| 70% | 92% | 74% |

Table 11.4. The effects of louping ill on the production of young grouse. This table shows the proportion of grouse proving seropositive to the virus, the estimated proportion of grouse that have been exposed and the scale of the mortality caused by the virus. When the proportion of young grouse tested in the shooting season shows more than 5% are positive to louping ill then the disease has caused significant mortality.

## 11.5 Strategy for controlling louping ill

- The strategy for controlling louping ill in a grouse population is first to reduce the contact rate between ticks and grouse and second to reduce the proportion of ticks that carry the virus.

- Reducing the tick contact rate requires a reduction in the survival of ticks. This is achieved by killing ticks before they reach a host, removing hosts so ticks never obtain a host meal and thus die, and placing an acaricide (anti-tick) drug on the hosts to kill ticks once they reach the host.

- Ticks require humidity to survive, particularly while off the host and when questing for a host. They obtain this by spending part of the year in the damp mat at the base of unpalatable vegetation. Reducing the vegetation that forms this mat reduces humidity and tick survival.

- Removing alternative hosts and treating sheep and other domestic stock with an acaricide will prevent ticks surviving to the next tick stage.

## 11.6  Reducing tick habitats

- A careful map of areas where ticks are abundant and where they are rare should be constructed by examining animals shot from the ground and from blanket drags.

- On some grouse moors, ticks are restricted to specific areas of bracken or grass ground. These areas can be converted to vegetation that does not favour ticks and improved grouse production may result.

- One grouse moor in northern England eradicated bracken from the lower ground to remove ticks and established a new grouse drive producing 60 additional brace a year.

- Removal of bracken is summarised in Chapter 5 and grass control in Chapter 6.

## 11.7 Reducing tick hosts

- There are two approaches to reducing tick abundance on hosts. The first is by dipping domestic stock and the second by reducing the abundance of alternative hosts.

- Shepherds dip their stock for a number of reasons and if you believe they are dipping against ticks it is essential to check that they are using long lasting acaricides that *will* kill ticks. A number of shepherds say they are dipping against tick but in fact they are dipping against scab and not against ticks. To satisfy yourself, help the shepherd dip or at least check the used containers.

- Ewes should be dipped at least twice during the summer. Once before going to the hill after lambing and again at clipping. Long lasting acaricides should be used at the correct concentration, these include Bayticol or some other persistent, pyrethroid based dips.

- During dipping care should be taken that sheep are properly immersed and that the efficacy of the dip is not reduced through running too many sheep through the dip – known as stripping. The recommended dosing rate should be strictly adhered to. As the quantity of dip is reduced during dipping, fresh dip should be added to maintain the concentration.

- Shepherds used to be afraid of dipping lambs since they were worried this would result in lambs being rejected by their mothers: mothering-up problems. Now with pour-on acaricides (e.g. Cypor, Vector, Provinec, Spot-on), lambs – and of course ewes – can be treated at regular intervals without being dipped.

- Ideally lambs should be treated with pour-ons every 4 to 6 weeks.

- Tick abundance is encouraged both by damp matt layer in the vegetation and the abundance of suitable hosts, particularly mammalian hosts. Ticks will feed on  most mammals but the main hosts are sheep, deer and hares. Reducing numbers of these hosts should lead to a significant reduction in ticks.

## 11.8  Control of louping ill within hosts

- The best and most effective method of controlling tick borne disease is to eliminate the ticks but this may prove almost impossible if ticks are widely distributed and abundant.

- Louping ill is effectively controlled by reducing the disease in alternative hosts that may help sustain the disease. The effect on grouse populations is so large that it seems most unlikely that the disease could be sustained by grouse themselves. Either way a grouse moor with few mammals would not support a tick population.

- Louping ill is controlled in sheep through vaccination. If the disease is highly prevalent in the sheep population the shepherd should be vaccinating his hoggs to protect his flock.

- The general and logical strategy is that only replacement hoggs need to be vaccinated since the adult sheep will have acquired natural immunity and the lambs should be protected by the antibodies passed to the lamb in the first milk, the colostrum. However the antibodies in the lamb wane over time and unless challenged at a young age, a lamb may become susceptible to infection when only 10 weeks of age.

- Some shepherds give their lambs a half dose of vaccine when about 12 weeks of age. This should be highly effective and could be a necessary approach to eliminating the disease. The approach can be expensive but if it eliminates the disease could be worth it financially and could be paid for by the increased grouse shooting.

- An alternative to lamb vaccination is to ensure the lambs are covered well with acaricide for the summer months and thus incapable of amplifying the disease.

- Hogg vaccination should be undertaken as a matter of course. The ideal time to vaccinate is a week before the tick rise starts in late April or when hoggs are run to the hill. All replacement sheep introduced onto a hill with louping ill should be vaccinated.

- While deer and hares do not produce a viraemic response capable of actively passing the virus to ticks, there is new evidence to suggest that they may well act as passive hosts, allowing virus to pass between ticks. While this process has not been confirmed in deer, control of deer and hares will help to reduce disease levels and may be necessary for disease elimination.

## CHAPTER TWELVE

# Grouse Chicks and Insects

Grouse chicks require a good protein source during their first few weeks of life so they can grow, develop their guts and be capable of flight. They usually obtain this protein by eating insects, particularly during the first two weeks of life. Without sufficient protein the chicks fail to grow and are susceptible to death through poor weather conditions or other causes.

## 12.1 Grouse chicks and insects: the biology

- Grouse chicks must obtain sufficient protein during their first two weeks of life to be able to grow to a size where they can fly and escape predators and to develop their own heat regulation.

- Heather does not provide sufficient protein for the young chicks and they obtain most of this protein by eating the relatively digestible insects. They will also eat the capsules of mosses and anything else available and suitable.

- On damp areas of blanket bog, insect production during early June should be high, with ample numbers of insects for the birds to feed upon. On drier, freely drained moorland, insects may be sparse and after hatching the hens usually take their broods to insect rich areas.

- Bog flushes, wet green areas with mosses and rushes are 18 times more productive of insects than mature heather moorland.

- Chicks eat a wide range of slow moving obvious insects. Their favourites include daddy-long-legs, small flies and click beetles.

## 12.2  Assessing insect abundance

• Determining whether a lack of insects is seriously reducing the production of grouse from your moor is not simple.

• In a poor breeding year, grouse broods in the July count will not only provide a low young:hen ratio but examination of the brood count will show few good broods and many small broods with just a few chicks.

• The brood count will also indicate a large proportion of cheepers or chicks of small size. These cheepers are often referred to as 'second broods' but are usually a combination of late and slow growing broods that have suffered from a lack of insect food.

• One of the best ways of determining if chicks are obtaining sufficient protein is to examine the droppings of young chicks less than 10 days of age (i.e. just before they can fly short distances). Roost sites can be found on the hill and if the odd chick is seen and caught it will often leave a dropping on your hand within a few moments. Smear these droppings out, if you can see plenty of black insect legs, wings and the remains of insects then it is clear that the chicks are finding insects well. However if the droppings are green with no black insect remains then a lack of insects may be the problem.

• Examine the areas where insects should be abundant – the wet boggy areas. If you lie down next to one of these on a still summer day the vegetation should be crawling with lots of small insects that a grouse chick can catch.


## 12.3  Poor insect abundance

• Poor insect abundance is caused by one or a combination of three factors: weather conditions, dryness and grazing pressure. It is also possible that continued heavy burning reduces the suitability of peat and *Sphagnum* for the insects to lay their eggs.

- Insects on moorland usually have an annual cycle, laying eggs one year that hatch and breed in the next. The survival of these insects is very dependent on wetness. When summers are dry the young insect stages do not survive well and consequently there are few insects in the following year. Note that dry weather conditions one year influence the insects the next. As a rule, poor insect abundance is a consequence of dry conditions in the preceding year rather than cold conditions in the current year.

- Cold temperatures in a year reduce the speed of the insects and not necessarily their hatching rate or survival. Indeed cold temperatures may slow insects down so grouse chicks find it easier to catch them but of course the coldness means the grouse chicks have less time to feed and must spend more time being brooded by the hen.

- Heavy grazing pressure reduces the amount of green vegetation that insects can feed on and has a large impact on the abundance of insects present.

- Reduced grazing pressure may improve insect numbers and chick survival.

## 12.4 Artificial bog flushes

- Since insects require wet areas to breed successfully, one approach to improving insect abundance is to build artificial bog flushes; damp areas with *Sphagnum*.

- The simplest way to produce an artificial bog flush is to block up drains in a way which reduces water flow. Adding some nutrients to the system is often a good idea and loose limestone chippings can be placed at the bottom of the drain. Clumps of *Sphagnum* moss should be added to provide a suitable habitat.

- In areas where no suitable habitat exists it may be necessary to build a shallow dam, introduce limestone chippings and *Sphagnum* and let the dam overflow down the hill producing a wet boggy area. Such an approach may require suitable digging equipment.

# CHAPTER THIRTEEN

# Counting and Assessing Grouse Populations

Grouse are a crop and before shooting starts an assessment of the potential harvest is necessary. Farmers never cut their hay or wheat without an inspection of the crop and financiers should never sell their investments without checking their current value. Likewise you should have a fair idea of your grouse population before shooting them.

## 13.1 Assessing your grouse population

- July counts are an essential part of grouse moor management. They not only provide a guide to the harvest but also an accurate measure of breeding success and perhaps some clues as to the problems of poor breeding.

- Many estates also undertake a spring count or pairs count in early April. This allows a coarse but early estimate of the potential harvest and is useful at a time when the owner or factor is letting shooting.

- Spring counts are likely to have some kind of error since there may still be birds which have yet to move onto the area to breed and some birds from snowy areas may still be in packs. Spring counts should be undertaken as late as possible before breeding commences. In most cases they can be undertaken in late March in northern England or mid-April in northern Scotland, after burning has stopped.

- Two types of counts can be undertaken, block counts and transect counts. Block counts are total counts; they are accurate and comparable between years and between places. Transect counts are estimated counts, suffer from errors but provide a wider picture of the moor. They can be comparable between years but not usually between areas.

## 13.2  Counting with dogs

- The most essential part of the equipment for conducting counts is a well trained and biddable dog. Without doubt the best breeds are the pointers and setters. Only with a pointer or setter can a wide beat of ground be counted accurately.

- Labradors and spaniels are wonderful dogs but are specifically bred for flushing and retrieving game. Should you use these for your counts you should ensure you are only using dogs that will not catch game and dogs that will cover the ground. A dog at heel or working in close is of little use in making an accurate grouse count.

- Pointers and setters must be well trained to cover a standard beat, hold their point and not chase game. The dogs should stay on point and hold the game until the handler can walk up to the dog, count and age all the birds flushed and record the presence of the adult hen and cock. Obtaining a measure of the average number of young produced per hen is important.

- The breed of pointer or setter is not that important – if you have a well bred dog the limiting factor is the dog's training and its handler. English Pointers, English Setters and Irish Setters all work elegantly and cover the ground well; they tend to mature later than some other breeds and require a firm training hand. With the pure pointing breeds, the show strains and the working strains are separate. The show strain is a different dog in looks and ability but the working strain is invariably of good quality.

- Some of the hunt point and retrieve (HPR) breeds can also provide a good service. Some are quick to learn and can have good stamina although few tend to work as elegantly as the pure pointing breeds. In these breeds the show and working strains tend to be inter-bred and there are a lot of poor and mediocre working dogs, even though they are nice pets. Nevertheless, a few breeders have outstanding HPRs. There are some particularly fine German Pointers about but you have to look for them.

- Dogs are always for sale in *The Shooting Times* and dog handlers often sell trained dogs. One of the problems of keeping a trained pointer is that keepers leave them in the kennel for most of the year and then pick them up in July and expect the dog to work perfectly. A dog needs regular work and training, the old adage of little and often counts for pointers.

- Experience with grouse is always important. Get the dog's nose 'turned on' to grouse and finding grouse and give the dog experience at regular intervals. We train our pointers and setters to find grouse nests, grouse chicks, dead grouse and to conduct grouse counts several months each year.

## 13.3  Block counts

- The block count for grouse was initiated by David Jenkins and Adam Watson in the 1950s. Block counts provide a total count and should be undertaken so the errors in estimation are small.

- Choice of the count area is important but there are no reasons why several count areas cannot be made, one on each beat or even each drive. Ideally these occupy a representative part of the moor or beat and are usually chosen as being central. An alternative method is to select the area directly in front of the butts.

- Some of the best places to count are sides of hills or basins where most of the site is visible.

- The ideal size of the block is 1 square kilometre, about 250 acres. One person with a reasonable dog can count this in about two and a half hours. After about this period the dog starts slowing down and concentration wanes.

- Mark the boundaries of the count area by knocking in a fence post at one corner and then measuring out 1000m along each of

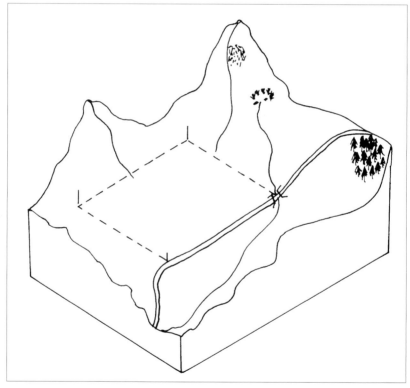

*An ideal 1km square for a block count of grouse – easily visible and properly staked out.*

the four sides. We prefer to place the count area in a north-south, east-west direction and then walk the sides on a compass bearing.

- Each corner should be marked with a post, preferably with the top painted white so you can see it while conducting your counts. We also like to have 6 posts up each side as reference points for the start of each walking beat but some estates feel this is too much. An alternative method is to have the count area abutting a line of butts and to use these as reference points.

## 13.4  Undertaking block counts

- July counts should be conducted when the young birds are strong on the wing, at least a week before shooting starts. Usually these counts are in the last two weeks of the month.

- Conduct the counts as early in the day as possible, soon after dawn. The dew helps with the scent and there should be ample scent around the roosting areas. Ideally you should be finished by 9.00am. In the heat of the day, dogs get tired, run with their mouths open, miss scent, the scent gets poor and broods may move into marginal areas to avoid the heat.

- Before your first count, spend some time walking and undertaking some dummy counts to see where the birds fly when disturbed and under what wind conditions. Usually it is best to have a slight breeze at an angle across the count area that pushes the birds down hill. You start counting at the bottom, flushing the broods onto ground already counted.

- Counts should not be conducted in strong winds, low cloud or rain or other weather conditions that may hinder the count or upset the birds.

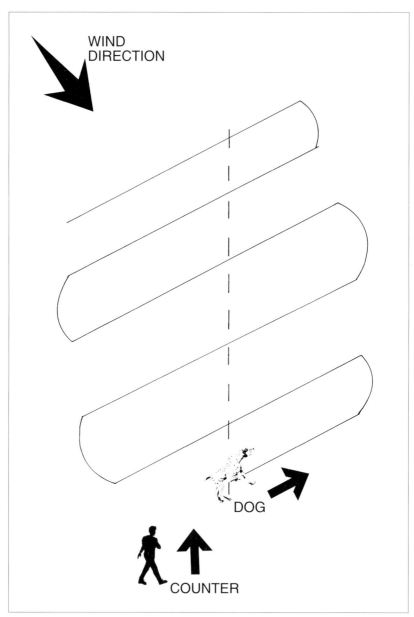

WIND
DIRECTION

DOG

COUNTER

*The principles of counting grouse using a dog.*

- The block is usually traversed in 6 parallel passes but 8 may be necessary depending on the area covered by the dog and the density of grouse. When grouse are abundant the dogs tend to have a tighter beat but at these times it is a good idea to have two or three dog handlers walking in parallel.

- If 6 passes are being undertaken, the first should be about 85m from the corner with 165m between each subsequent beat. This allows the dog to range about 85m either side of you on a standard beat. You should encourage your dog and ensure it covers the ground thoroughly.

- When the dog goes on point, leave your pass line, walk to the dog, flush the grouse and record sex and number of adults and the number of young. After you are sure all birds have been counted, send the dog out on its beat while you return to your original line.

- When densities are medium to low it is a good idea to carry a map and record the location of each brood so a series of maps can be collated over the year.

- At the end of the count express your count as the number of birds per square kilometre (250 acres) and the average number of young per hen. Record the number of 'barren pairs' – these are failed breeders, not truly barren. You can make estimates for the beat by multiplying up to the corrected area, although care should be taken not to over-extrapolate these estimates.

- Grouse moors usually shoot between 30% and 50% of their birds depending on density, conditions and whether the population is rising. Over a number of years the counts provide a very accurate guide to what can be expected in the season and will thus be most helpful to the shoot manager.

## 13.5  Transect counts

- Transect counts provide a wider but less accurate picture of the grouse population and allow a sample count of breeding production.

- Transect counts are from one point to the next, the total walk taking about two and a half hours to be equivalent in area to a block count of 1 square kilometre (250 acres).

- Transect counts tend to be conducted by a single individual who knows the path walked each year, thus providing comparisons between years. However these transects should be marked with several stakes so others can repeat the counts in years to come.

- Transect counts are best conducted on each of the drives of the moor. Start at butt 3 and walk the drive for an hour and quarter before taking a return beat 150m parallel to the first to arrive back at butt 6.

- Again take care to keep your line, ensure the dog covers the ground well and take extra care not to double count some broods. A map that marks the position and movement of each brood can be very helpful.

- As with block counts, record the number of adults, age, sex and number of young.

# CHAPTER FOURTEEN

# Shooting and Ageing Grouse

This is a short chapter for such a large subject. In essence this chapter summarises some details about shooting grouse while giving more detailed information on ageing and sexing grouse. Siting butts and driving grouse is not a simple matter and guidance on this requires a detailed plan for each estate and a site visit by an experienced Game Conservancy Ltd Advisor.

## 14.1 Strategies for harvesting grouse

- The red grouse shooting season starts on 12 August and runs until 10 December. Most grouse shooting occurs during the first six weeks of the season.

- By October the grouse have usually become 'wild and jumpy' and most estates have stopped shooting because of the difficulties of harvesting a reasonable number of grouse, the difficult weather conditions that prevail at this time of year, the need to cull deer and problems with obtaining numbers of experienced beaters.

- If a large number of grouse need to be harvested then the main bag must be taken early in the season with the majority harvested before the middle of September.

- Young hen grouse will start dispersing from high density grouse areas as early as August and dispersal may well continue into December. The grouse should be harvested early in the season. Excess numbers killed during the early part of the season may be compensated for through immigration of birds. Shooting later in the season may well reduce potential breeding stock.

- As a rule it is wise to shoot or at least drive each beat in each year, even if the decision is made not to shoot any grouse. Note that bird movements and warm weather conditions may produce a blank early in the shooting season but provide rewarding shooting by the middle of September.

- Each beat should ideally be shot once and then rested for a two week period; shooting more frequently than this may provide a smaller bag overall since birds have not been allowed to settle after shooting.

## 14.2 Shooting over pointers

- The grouse world is divided into those who enjoy shooting over pointers, watching the dogs being worked during a quiet day on the hill with some friends and those who feel the only form of grouse shooting is a highly organised, challenging and productive driven grouse day. They are different sports and there is no reason why people should not enjoy both.

- Shooting over pointers is generally undertaken early in the season when the broods are still in family coveys and before the birds become too jumpy. Some estates just shoot marginal ground in the first few days of the season and use the pointers for a quiet day with inexperienced Guns.

- While a few estates still maintain their own pointer kennels, most must hire an experienced person to run his dogs. He will probably bring three or more dogs and run each at 20-30 minute intervals. The handler should say what he expects from the Guns and others. He will not expect to carry the game shot and will expect all Guns to be experienced and safe both for the dogs and himself.

- On a pointer day, the ideal is to have four Guns for every dog handler, walking  behind the dog. The first beat is usually into or across the wind and Guns should ensure they are never standing upwind of the working dog.

- When the dog goes on point the handler will usually hold his hand up or make some sign that he believes the dog is on game. The two nearest Guns then approach the pointing dog from behind until they are level with the dog but some 3-5m away. The handler will then send the dog in and the Guns walk forward slowly taking note of the location of the dog, handler and others involved in the party.

- Usually the cock will break first and will call and there is a good opportunity of shooting two birds from the covey. Guns should shoot birds breaking on their side of the pointer.

- After a covey has been flushed and a bird or two shot, the handler may send his dog in to check that there are no other birds still sitting. When his dog has finished he will call it back and place on a lead. At this stage the Guns may then send in their retriever or spaniel to collect the shot bird. Nothing is more annoying for a dog handler to have other dogs jumping around in front of a pointer on point.

- With good dogs and good Guns it is possible to shoot many grouse and greatly reduce the size of the grouse population. Wisely some estates ask Guns to shoot cocks only and while a little experience may be needed (see 14.6), this is a sensible approach for low density populations.

- There are no hard and fast rules about dog breeds; experience in dogs and handler are more important. Good English Pointers, English Setters and Irish Setters will cover the ground elegantly while well bred and run German Pointers and Brittany Spaniels will not be so classy but may have more stamina and be more biddable.

## 14.3 Walked up rough shooting

- Walked up rough shooting with a couple of Guns and a couple of dogs with the potential of a mixed bag can provide an enjoyable and challenging day of sport.

- One of the most popular day's shooting frequently involves the opportunity to shoot both some red grouse and some ptarmigan and, if the season has started, the odd wild pheasant.

- Such days should cover marginal ground but care should always be taken to ensure Guns keep their own dogs under control and follow the Countryside Code. Special care should be taken with stock, walls and gates.

- If the day is let to a team, a keeper will need to go with the Guns and show them where they can walk and what they can shoot. The keeper will probably have to carry most of the shot game.

## 14.4 Driven grouse shooting

- A driven day's grouse shooting with a full team of Guns and a bag of less than 35 brace is likely to mean that some of the Guns may not have shot a bird.

- Most estates have traditions for organising a driven day, with set ideas on the number of beaters required, how to drive the ground and where lunch will be arranged. Siting the butts and the way of driving grouse varies so much depending on terrain, grouse density, prevailing wind and other factors that these are best left to decisions by each estate. Assistance can be obtained from Game Conservancy Ltd's Advisory Department (01425 652381).

- Most driven days involve between 4 and 6 drives, have nine Guns and 16 beaters.

*Above: Correct siting of butts is vital to presenting good driven grouse. This temporary butt is built of heather bales.*

*Below: A permanent butt in stone and capped with living heather.*

- Guns should be in their butts before the drive starts and have made a mental note of the position of all flankers, pickers up and other Guns. As a rule pegs stuck in the butt are useful to prevent a gun swinging onto a neighbouring Gun.

- People attending a shoot should not wear brightly coloured clothes, while a hat helps to prevent reflection from the forehead. It is amazing how grouse will avoid butts when they see an obvious head and shoulders protruding.

- Note the position of all birds shot to assist with picking up.

- On many shoots a horn or whistle will be blown when the line of beaters is in shot, at this point no more grouse should be taken in front of the butts and only safe birds shot behind them.

- Nobody should leave their butt until every beater is in and the final horn blown.

- After a drive collect your empty cartridges and leave the game you have shot prominently on top of the butt to be collected.

## 14.5  Ageing grouse

- After a day's grouse shooting it is traditional to count the bag and record the relative proportion of young and old grouse.

- Recording the ratio of young to old grouse is generally considered a reflection of how well the grouse have bred that season. Unfortunately this is not really the case. The proportion of young birds in the bag shows little relationship to the actual breeding production of the population because of the weather conditions and behaviour of the birds on the shooting day. Counting grouse in July is the best method for assessing the breeding production of grouse.

- Ageing grouse and inspecting the condition of the birds in the game larder before the game dealer collects the carcasses is wise. It allows the game manager and keeper to inspect and assess the condition of the birds and to obtain an estimate of the value of the bag before the game dealer arrives.

- There can be a difference of interest between the game dealer and the estate. The game dealer will pay more for young grouse than old grouse and will look to see that the bag division errs in his favour. The estate wants the money from the bag to pay for the beaters and the other costs of a day's grouse shooting, so will tend to err in the other direction and over-emphasise the proportion of young. Dividing the bag before the dealer comes allows the dealer to inspect the bag and make any comments on birds he feels have been misclassified.

- As a rule it is wise to use a combination of techniques to age grouse and three techniques should be undertaken on each bird. We recommend examination of the primaries, skull thickness and the toe nails.

- *Third feather short in young birds.* The moult of young grouse leaves the outer 2 primary feathers unmoulted so that by August most of the young birds have the third primary feather shorter than expected. Old birds moult *all* their primaries and thus by August outer primary 1 or primary 2 have been or are just about to be moulted and shorter than expected. However, care should be taken since late breeding birds, particularly if they are diseased, may have only just moulted their third primary and the old bird at first glance looks like a young bird. If the outer primaries are very worn and are much lighter in colour and other attributes indicate an old bird, the bird is probably old.

- *Skull soft and easily crushed in young birds.* The skull of young birds is relatively soft. This is best tested by hanging the bird by its head from your first and second finger and then pushing the

159

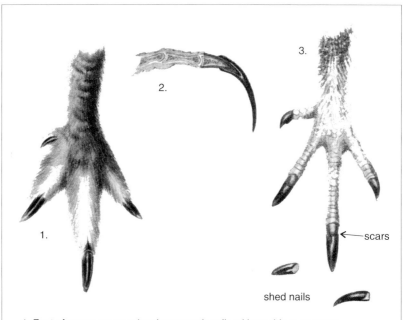

1. Foot of young grouse showing smooth nails with no ridges or scars.
2. Vertical section of nail with old nail ready to be shed.
3. Foot of old grouse showing scars where last years nails have been shed.

end of your thumb into the middle of the skull. If the skull is soft and your thumb crushes the skull easily then this is clearly a young bird. A great deal of strength, enough to hurt your thumb, would be needed to crush the skull of an old bird. Try a few birds out and it should be quite clear which are old and which are young.

•   *Presence of toe nail scars in old birds.* Old birds moult their toe nails each autumn and while few have started by August, most old birds have shed their toe nails by September, leaving a character-istic ridge across the toe nail. This is not a good way of ageing grouse at the beginning of the season but later in the season, as the young grouse mature it becomes a more important technique.

160

An obvious scar on the toenail shows an old bird but the absence of such a scar does not prove the bird is young.

- *Inspection of gonads.* Birds that have bred often show larger gonads than young birds. In particular, inspection of the ovaries of a hen that has bred will show a number of still large but collapsed follicles whereas young hens only have small undeveloped ovaries (For inspecting gonads see 14.6).

- *Leg strength.* The lower legs of the young bird will break more easily than those of an old bird. As with the skull, hold the leg of the dead bird between your thumb and first two fingers; if you can break the leg then this would indicate that the bird was probably young, while the leg bone of an old bird is difficult to break. Such comparisons are only relative and there is always the problem that a strong fisted keeper can break all the bones without noticing the difference!

## 14.6  Sexing grouse

- A number of characteristics of the grouse can be used to determine the bird's sex, although care is always needed. There are some dark large hens and a few cocks which show all the characteristics of a hen.

- *Gonad inspection.* The best method for sexing a grouse is to inspect the bird's gonads, although this can only be done with a dead bird. Remove the guts from the bird and then peer into the body cavity. On the upper side of the body, forward of the kidneys, lie the gonads.

- In males there are two distinct cream coloured oval testicles. In the hen the ovaries are two distinct yellowy white masses of small eggs. The ovary on the right is very small and the one on the left is relatively well developed.

- During the breeding season the ovaries can look like a tiny bunch of grapes with a well developed and muscular oviduct.

- *Comb size and colour.* As a rule cocks have a larger and deeper reddish coloured comb above the eyes.

- *Size of bird.* Cocks usually weigh more and are bigger boned than hen grouse.

- *Plumage colour.* Cocks usually have a dark rich reddish plumage while the hens tend to have a more yellow and speckled plumage. However this difference is far from certain and many cocks can look like hens and hens like cocks.

- *Calling behaviour.* Only cocks perform the distinctive song flight.

## 14.7 Grouse management records

- Well kept records are essential for the keeper, factor and moor owner. They provide the detailed information on good and poor years and can help identify problems in grouse production.

- Keepers should keep a diary with general comments on activities, counts, trap records and burning. These are often useful to refer back to in following years.

- Keepers should keep monthly counts and a detailed map of all predators seen and killed.

- Bag records from each beat and counts from each beat should be carefully tabulated and compared over a period of years.

- The owner or factor will wish to keep a detailed game book and keep a note of the keeper's counts and observations to compare and analyse.

# CHAPTER FIFTEEN

# Birds and the Law

Today, more than ever before, keepers and moor owners must be aware of the law. Recent changes in the law quite often lead to confusion on certain aspects, so it seems worthwhile running through the status and protection offered to several upland bird species. Laws on heather burning and other activities are covered elsewhere in the relevant chapters.

This chapter provides some guidelines; it is not a legal document but a guide to help you. The authors take no responsibility for errors or omissions. We would like to thank staff of the RSPB for their assistance in the production of this chapter.

## 15.1  Wildlife and Countryside Act

- The heather moorlands of Britain are home to an internationally important assemblage of bird species.

- While some of these birds may not appear rare to the moor owner or his keeper, several of them have specific protection under legislation laid down by the EU and by Parliament. Details of their current (1994) population size and trend are summarised in Table 15.1.

- The primary legislation protecting birds and governing keepers and their activities is the Wildlife and Countryside Act 1981.

- In essence, the law protects all birds, their eggs and nests if in use. Some exceptions occur and gamebirds are not covered by the Wildlife and Countryside Act.

- The gamebirds, in particular the pheasant, partridge species, black grouse, red grouse, ptarmigan and capercaillie are covered in the Game Acts.

- The Wildlife and Countryside Act groups birds into a number of different schedules. The important schedules as far as keepering and moorland birds are concerned are the Specially Protected Species in Schedule 1 and the Sporting Birds in Schedule 2 Part I. The pest species used to be in Schedule 2 Part II but are now covered under a General Licence.

- It is worth noting that all birds, nests and eggs are protected and it is an offence to:
  - kill, injure or take a wild bird
  - damage, destroy or take the egg or nest (when in use) of any wild bird
  - possess or control any wild bird, egg or part of a bird which has been taken from the wild in contravention of the law.

| Species | UK Population (Pairs) | % EC Population | Trend |
|---|---|---|---|
| Golden eagle | 510 | 25% | Stable |
| Hen harrier | 550 | 24% | Increasing |
| Peregrine | 850 | 26% | Increasing |
| Merlin | 600 | 95% | Stable |
| Golden plover | 22,600 | 96% | Decreasing |
| Greenshank | 950 | 100% | Decreasing |
| Dunlin | 950 | 100% | Decreasing |
| Short eared owl | 1,000 | 80% | Stable |

Table 15.1. Moorland nesting birds provided with special protection under Annexe 1 of The European Union Directive on the Conservation of Wild Birds and/or Schedule 1 of The Wildlife and Countryside Act.

## 15.2 Schedule 1 birds

- Schedule 1 birds have special protection and special penalties result if they are taken or disturbed. While the list is long, the principle upland species include:

| | | |
|---|---|---|
| Crossbill species | Greenshank | Redwing |
| Diver species | Harrier species | Whooper Swan |
| Dotterel | Red Kite | Bewick Swan |
| Golden eagle | Merlin | Whimbrel |
| White tailed Eagle | Osprey | |
| Gyr Falcon | Snowy Owl | |
| Fieldfare | Peregrine | |
| Goshawk | Barn Owl | |

- Under no circumstances can you kill, take, damage or destroy any of these birds, their nests (if in use) or their eggs.

- It is also an offence to disturb any bird species on Schedule 1 while it is nest building or is at or near a nest with eggs or young. Neither can you disturb the young of any Schedule 1 species. This means if you have a harrier, merlin or peregrine nesting on your ground you must take special care not to disturb it. As a keeper or landowner you should be aware if these species nest on your ground.

- Any person found guilty of an offence of killing or taking a Schedule 1 bird or using poison to kill birds is liable to a fine of up to £5000. For other offences the maximum fine is £1000. Each incident or each bird involved is considered a separate offence so the total fine is the multiple of the offences.

## 15.3 Pest species

- Certain pest species can be taken under General Licence. These licences are held by the Department of the Environment, Ministry of Agriculture, Fisheries and Food and the Scottish Office Environment Department. You do not have to apply for a General Licence.

- The licences automatically allow authorised persons to carry out the licensable act in England, Scotland and Wales. An authorised person is the owner or occupier of a piece of land on which the action takes place or any person authorised by the owner or occupier or the person with shooting or fishing rights. It can also be someone authorised by a local authority or government agency (EN, SNH, CCW, Water Authority etc.).

- There is a General Licence which allows the killing of certain birds to conserve wild birds. Authorised people can also kill or take certain birds including taking or destroying their eggs to prevent serious damage to livestock. These birds can be killed by shooting, a cage trap or hand held net.

- The only birds that can be taken or killed to conserve wild birds under this General Licence are:

  | | |
  |---|---|
  | Carrion/Hooded Crow | Herring Gull |
  | Jackdaw | Greater Black-backed gull |
  | Jay | Lesser Black-backed gull |
  | Magpie | Rook |
  | Feral Pigeon | |

- Note: raven, sparrowhawk, goshawk, buzzard, short eared owl and kestrel are protected at all times.

- Common gull and black-headed gull are also protected at all times (except at aerodromes for the purpose of preserving air safety and where there is no other course of action).

- There is a General Licence which permits the keeping or confining of certain species by an authorised person in Larsen traps for the express purpose of conserving wild birds or collections of wild birds. A live decoy is allowed in particular types of Larsen and cage traps providing the trap is inspected every 24 hours, the decoy is supplied with food, fresh water, a perch and some form of shelter. Decoys cannot be sold.

- Prohibited techniques for killing, taking or injuring birds (except under licence) include springs, gin traps, pole traps, snares, hook and line, electrical devices, poisonous or stupefying substances, nets, mist nests, gas or smoke, baited boards, bird lime or similar substances and chemical wetting agents, sound recordings, tethered birds as decoys and maimed birds.

- You are not allowed to kill birds with bows, crossbows, explosives other than ammunition, automatic or semi-automatic weapons capable of firing more than three shots. Neither can you use guns with an internal muzzle diameter greater than 1.75 inches, artificial light or dazzling devices and sights for night shooting.

- An authorised person can, under General Licence, use a semi-automatic weapon capable of firing more than three shots, to kill certain pest species for the purpose of preserving public health and preventing damage to agriculture but he would need a firearm certificate.

- You are not allowed to use any mechanically propelled vehicle to pursue a wild bird for capture or for killing.

## 15.4 Quarry species

- Schedule 2 Part I birds can be killed or taken outside the close season.

- Particular birds of interest to upland keepers and owners include, with the period of the open season:

| | | |
|---|---|---|
| Red Grouse | 12 August | 10 December |
| Ptarmigan | 12 August | 10 December |
| Black grouse | 20 August | 10 December |
| Capercaillie | 1 October | 31 January |
| Partridge species | 1 September | 1 February |
| Pheasant | 1 October | 1 February |
| Mallard | 1 September | 31 January (inland) |
| Golden Plover | 1 September | 31 January (inland) |
| Common Snipe | 12 August | 31 January (inland) |
| Teal | 1 September | 31 January (inland) |
| Woodcock | 1 October | 31 January (inland) |
| | 1 September | 31 January (in Scotland) |

- A number of orders prevent the Sunday shooting of Schedule 2 Part I quarry species in certain administrative counties of England and Wales. Shooting game species on Sunday and Christmas Day is illegal in Scotland.

## 15.5  Powers of the Police

- If a Police officer suspects any person of committing an offence involving wild birds he or she can:

- Stop and search that person or vehicle if the officer suspects evidence is to be found on that person or vehicle.

- Seize and detain anything which may be evidence of the offence or liable to forfeiture.

- Enter any land other than a dwelling house.

- With a warrant from a Justice of the Peace, search premises if he has reasonable grounds to suspect evidence may be found on the property or evidence of any offence incurring a special penalty, notably involving Schedule 1 species.

- The courts must confiscate any bird, nest, egg or skin involved in an offence. They may also confiscate any vehicle, animal, weapon or other object which was used to commit the offence.

# ARE YOU MAKING THE MOST OF YOUR MOOR?

Could practical professional advice improve the quality of your sport?
Game Conservancy Ltd's Advisory Service has been helping moor managers,
upland keepers, owners, lairds and shoot tenants on a wide range of grouse
and conservation matters for over fifty years.

We are acknowledged to be the leading experts in all aspects of
game and shoot management.

Backed by the scientific research of The Game Conservancy Trust,
our advisors are in a unique position to assist you in improving
the potential of your moor.

Some of the subjects we are asked about regularly include:

- *Disease control and red grouse*
- *Correct grazing and burning regimes*
- *Upland predation control*
- *Estimating populations and suggesting sustainable shooting levels*
- *Shoot cost analysis and financial planning*
- *Sporting valuations*
- *Improving the quality of drives*

To find out how we can help you, contact:

Game Conservancy Ltd   or   Game Conservancy Ltd
Fordingbridge                  Scottish Headquarters
Hampshire                     Couston, Newtyle
SP6 1EF                      Perthshire PH12 8UT

Tel:  01425 652381       Tel:  01828 650543
Fax: 01425 655848       Fax: 01828 650560

# GROUSE IN SPACE AND TIME

## The Population Biology of a Managed Gamebird

*"Long-term maintenance of red grouse populations must pivot on the care of their habitat. Balanced grazing and careful burning of heather are needed to prevent the degradation of moorland and the spread of coarse grasses and bracken. Given a suitable habitat, legal predator control is essential to limit the effects of predation and to achieve a sufficient density of grouse for driven shooting. Only then will the economic, social and conservation benefits of grouse management be fully realized."*

Dr. Peter Hudson's 280-page hardbacked review of red grouse research conducted by The Game Conservancy Trust.

Available for £25.00, including postage and packing. A gold-tooled, fully leather bound version is also available.

Orders and enquiries to:

The Sales Centre
Game Conservancy Ltd
Fordingbridge                          Tel:  01425 652381
Hampshire SP6 1EF                      Fax:  01425 655848